CW00666342

Pra

THE Nɪɴᴇ

"In *The Nine*, Phil Simon adroitly lays out the current landscape of emerging technologies. Readers will quickly grasp the importance and effects of today's most essential trends."

—JEREMY BAILENSON, Thomas More Storke Professor of Communication, Stanford University and author of *Experience on Demand*

"A must-read for every leader in every company. *The Nine* is a timely, realistic, inspiring, and sometimes scary book about the new world of work. Read it and weep (or reap)!"

—JAY BAER, coauthor of *Talk Triggers: The Complete Guide to Creating Customers with Word of Mouth*

"*The Nine* is a dynamic and essential book on the future of the workplace, deftly navigating the implications as a wave of new technology crashes into decades of tradition."

—ALEX KANTROWITZ, host of the *Big Technology* podcast and author of *Always Day One: How the Tech Titans Plan to Stay on Top Forever*

"Never before has the workplace been as confusing and dynamic as it is today—and things will only intensify in the years ahead. Simon provides much-needed analysis, synthesis, and guidance."

—GERALD C. KANE, C. Herman and Mary Virginia Terry chair in business administration at the University of Georgia and coauthor of *The Technology Fallacy*

"The past few years have been a blur of confusion for leaders and employees. Fortunately, Phil Simon cuts through the clutter and points out the few signals in the workplace you can't afford to dismiss as noise."

—DAVID BURKUS, author of *Best Team Ever* and
Leading From Anywhere

"Technology, economy, business models … In *The Nine*, Simon pushes you beyond the five or six issues you likely have on your radar. You'll gain a clearer view of the forces coming together and see new opportunities—and risks. Be prepared. Be ahead."

—TERRI GRIFFITH, Keith Beedie chair in innovation
and entrepreneurship, Simon Fraser University
and author of *The Plugged-In Manager*

"In an increasingly complex world, Phil Simon does us a great service by simplifying the sources of the seismic shifts we see all around us. I dog-eared the crap out of it for future reference."

—KARIN REED, CEO of Speaker Dynamics and coauthor of
Suddenly Hybrid: Managing the Modern Meeting

THE
NINE

EX LIBRIS

Russ Maney

THE
NINE

THE TECTONIC FORCES RESHAPING THE WORKPLACE

PHIL SIMON

Award-winning author of *Project Management in the Hybrid Workplace* and *Low-Code/No-Code*

RACKET

Gilbert, AZ

Copyrighted Material

The Nine: The Tectonic Forces Reshaping the Workplace

Copyright © 2023 by Phil Simon. All rights reserved.

No part of this publication may be reproduced, stored in a retrieval system, or transmitted, in any form or by any means—electronic, mechanical, photocopying, recording, or otherwise—without prior written permission from the publisher, except for the inclusion of brief quotations in a review.

For information about this title or to order other books and/or electronic media, contact the publisher:

Racket Publishing | www.racketpublishing.com

Hardcover ISBN: 979-8-985814774
Paperback ISBN: 979-8-985814767
ebook ISBN: 979-8-985814781

Printed in the United States of America

Cover design: Luke Fletcher | www.fletcherdesigns.com
Interior design: Jessica Angerstein

Also by Phil Simon

The Future of Work

Reimagining Collaboration: Slack, Microsoft Teams, Zoom, and the Post-COVID World of Work (Book 1)

Project Management in the Hybrid Workplace (Book 2)

Low-Code/No-Code: Citizen Developers and the Surprising Future of Business Applications (Book 3)

Other Books

Zoom For Dummies

Agile: The Insights You Need from Harvard Business Review (contributor)

Slack For Dummies

Analytics: The Agile Way

Message Not Received: Why Business Communication Is Broken and How to Fix It

The Visual Organization: Data Visualization, Big Data, and the Quest for Better Decisions

Too Big to Ignore: The Business Case for Big Data

The Age of the Platform: How Amazon, Apple, Facebook, and Google Have Redefined Business

The New Small: How a New Breed of Small Businesses Is Harnessing the Power of Emerging Technologies

The Next Wave of Technologies: Opportunities in Chaos

Why New Systems Fail: An Insider's Guide to Successful IT Projects

In gratitude to Dr. Ugur Sahin and Dr. Özlem Türeci.

"For every action, there is an equal
and opposite reaction."

—NEWTON'S THIRD LAW

"Worlds are colliding."

—JASON ALEXANDER AS GEORGE COSTANZA,
SEINFELD, "THE POOL GUY"

CONTENTS

LIST OF FIGURES AND TABLES

INTRODUCTION

This is not a tactical book.

"Enlightenments, like accidents, happen only to prepared minds."
—HERB SIMON

Last year, I had an epiphany: a common thread had undergirded my previous three texts. That is, I had unwittingly written a multibook series about the exciting, challenging, and dramatically different future of work.

Let me explain.

Reimagining Collaboration hit the shelves in December 2020. At a high level, the book explored the power of internal collaboration hubs. Think of Zoom as Skype 2.0 if you like. Dismiss Microsoft Teams and Slack as souped-up versions of email. Many have, and I can't stop you from doing the same. But you're missing out on ways to dramatically improve how you collaborate with others.

Project Management in the Hybrid Workplace dropped eighteen months later. Let's hope that its title is pretty self-explanatory. No one would ever call project management easy, but remote and hybrid work represent additional, formidable obstacles that inhibit employees, teams, departments, and even entire companies from getting things done.

Arriving in November 2022, *Low-Code/No-Code* delved into the burgeoning citizen development movement. People who want to build valuable business apps no longer need to know how to code. The implications for IT departments, nontechies, and the future of work are profound.

Each book examined a single topic. As such, each required a narrow and deep emphasis.

This book takes a decidedly different tack. This next installment in my accidental series identifies nine separate but related forces that are reshaping the workplace.

Setting Expectations

Each of the following nine chapters covers one of these forces, with a specific focus on how it affects the world of work. Chapter 10 brings it all home.

No book of any reasonable length can tell you everything you need to know about automation, blockchain, generative artificial intelligence (AI), immersive technologies, and the rest of the topics in the upcoming pages. *The Nine* is no exception to this rule. Authors have penned lengthy texts on these evolving topics, with more undoubtedly on the way. Know this going in: we're about to cover a great deal of ground. Think wide, not deep.

In these chapters, readers will find what I believe to be the most valuable information on each force. I also describe many of their interrelationships and ways that they'll collide.

At a high level, *The Nine* aspires to inform, provoke, and make you think. You may take issue with some of my analyses, recommendations, predictions, and conclusions. I'm entirely comfortable with that. Intelligent and reasonable people can disagree.

Lastly, this book examines the future workplace through a strategic lens. You won't find step-by-step instructions for achieving specific tactical objectives. If you're looking for a bunch of listicles and prescriptions that purport to guarantee successful outcomes, don't buy this book. You'll be disappointed.

Let's light this candle.

CHAPTER 1

Employee Empowerment

The relatively docile workforces of previous decades aren't returning.

"History never repeats itself, but it does often rhyme."

—MARK TWAIN

On November 1, 2018, thousands of employees at one of the largest, most powerful corporations the world has ever seen walked off the job.

Ring any bells? For several reasons, probably not. And why should it?

First, my description of the work stoppage was intentionally coy and vague. (Don't worry, we'll return to it shortly.)

Second, to put it mildly, the past five years have been a bit of a blur. The 24/7 media cycle makes it impossible to stay completely informed—at least if you want to maintain some semblance of sanity and actually do your job. Highlights and low points have abounded, although the latter seems to be winning the battle. Doomscrolling all day long just isn't healthy.

Third, labor management strife is old hat. Forget the halcyon days of US unions of the 1930s. Between 1973 and 2021, the Economic Policy Institute found that the median number of workers involved in major work stoppages in the United States was 191,500. Figure 1.1 provides an annual breakdown.

Number of US Workers Involved in Major Work Stoppages (1973–2021)

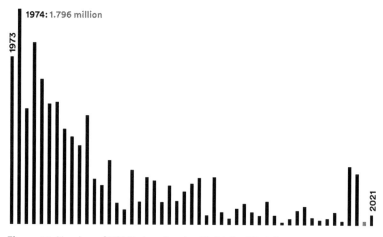

Figure 1.1: Number of US Workers Involved in Major Work Stoppages, 1973–2021
Source: Economic Policy Institute

The issues among specific conflicts vary, but money is almost always a bone of contention. Inflation-adjusted middle-class wages in the US have stagnated over the past four decades,[1] and workers have become restive. More went on strike in 2021 than in any year since 2005.[2]

So, what was so important about that November day nearly five years ago?

An Unprecedented Type of Employee Rebellion

On several levels, this particular workplace protest was arguably unlike any other. For starters, it didn't resemble traditional blue-collar clashes popularized in movies such as *Norma Rae*, for which Sally Field won the 1980 Academy Award for Best Actress. Apples and coconuts.

The aggrieved employees weren't slogging long hours at the local textile mill for minimum wage six days per week. Nor were they risking their lives each day like the United Mine Workers of America in Pennsylvania who struck and threatened to cut off the supply of fuel in the winter of 1902.

Also, consider the mutiny's sheer scale. Organizers estimated that, in total, more than 20,000 full-time employees and contractors staged the international one-day walkout.[3] As NPR reported, workers:

> walked out of Google offices at 11:10 a.m. local time Thursday in Singapore, Zurich, London, Dublin, and New York City, filling nearby streets, sidewalks, and parks. And in California, home to Google's headquarters, employees streamed out of its offices into plazas.[4]

Yes, the cat's finally out of the bag. I'm talking about Google.

Its workers organized in an organic, rapid, and decentralized manner. They eschewed formal meetings; meticulous planning this was not. No union organizers took part. In their stead, people relied on digital communication tools to coordinate their world-wide walkout—some of which Google had developed itself for internal use. (More than a little ironic.)

In other words, who needs arguably antiquated twentieth century constructs today when you've got a smartphone in your pocket? Whip it out and post to internal bulletin boards, Slack, Signal, Discord, and, of course, Twitter.

Tweets like the one in Figure 1.2 weren't uncommon on that fateful November day.

Figure 1.2: Tweet From Former Google Employee Jaana Dogan, Source: Twitter

Dogan's tweet revealed the source of the workers' rage.

By way of background, in 2014, the internet giant parted ways with one of its top executives, Andy Rubin. (Yes, the same Google gave the Father of Android a mind-boggling $90 million severance package.)

On October 25, 2018, the *New York Times* published an incendiary behind-the-scenes exposé detailing the previously clandestine circumstances behind his departure. From the piece:

> an employee had accused Mr. Rubin of sexual misconduct. The woman, with whom Mr. Rubin had been having an extramarital relationship, said he coerced her into performing

oral sex in a hotel room in 2013, according to two company executives with knowledge of the episode. Google investigated and concluded her claim was credible.[5]

This story was the spark that lit the fire. Disgruntlement among the rank and file had been growing for years, especially in the wake of #MeToo. Most relevant here, female workers had long objected to Google's treatment of women, handling of sexual assault cases, and requirement that all employees submit to forced arbitration as a condition of employment.

As the *Los Angeles Times* reported, Google employees weren't lacking for demands. They included:

- An end to forced arbitration for everyone—including temporary workers and contractors.
- The right to bring a coworker into every HR meeting.
- A commitment to end pay and opportunity inequity; provide data on compensation gaps by race, gender, and ethnicity; and make that data accessible to all Google and Alphabet* employees and contractors.
- A publicly disclosed sexual harassment transparency report. It would include the number of harassment claims at Google over time and by business area; the types of claims submitted; how many victims and accused have left Google; and details of any exit packages granted to executives accused of harassment.
- A clear and globally inclusive process for full-timers and contractors to anonymously report sexual misconduct; independence for HR to relieve the pressure to please senior management by downplaying claims.[6]

---

* Alphabet became Google's parent company in an October 2015 reorg.

Think for a moment about what Google employees *weren't* demanding. They were more than satisfied with their compensation and benefits. The company had long offered its employees generous time off and workplace perks to die for. That bawdy list included flexible work schedules, onsite medical assistance, free massages, dry cleaning, meals, snacks, and fitness facilities.[7]

And now, for the most remarkable part of the story. Google management publicly supported its employees' coordinated defiance. (Yes, you read that right.) Countless CEOs watched the company's reaction in amazement. More than a few took to Twitter and LinkedIn to express their bewilderment. Why would a company's leaders tolerate—much less support or tacitly endorse—this degree of insubordination?

When all was said and done, Google CEO Sundar Pichai acceded to most of his employees' requirements. Rather than declare war on his workforce, he struck a decidedly conciliatory tone. Speaking at the *New York Times* DealBook conference a few hours after the walkout began, he earnestly told the live audience, "Moments like this show that we didn't always get it right."[8]

Perhaps Pichai genuinely viewed the employees' demands to be sensible. (Rare is the individual who rises to the rank of CEO without being able to read the room.) Maybe he believed that Google's policies were overly restrictive and unfair to women. Odds are, though, that he and the top brass viewed the costs of *inaction* as unacceptable. Naturally, more than one thing can be true.

One thing, however, is certain: by placating its employees, the company could contain the situation and likely avoid the dreaded u-word (union).

Not long after Google's travails, another tech company wasn't so lucky.

Employee Relations Break Bad at Kickstarter

Since its launch in April 2009, the crowdfunding site Kickstarter benefited from a special employee-management relationship. The company had fostered a collaborative culture, and its workforce firmly believed in its mission "to help bring creative projects to life."[9]

In September 2015, Kickstarter received its certification as a Public Benefit Corporation or B Corp.[10] It had met "the highest standards of verified social and environmental performance, public transparency, and legal accountability to balance profit and purpose."[11] Its corporate charter formally recognized that it need not focus exclusively on maximizing profits. (Chapter 10 returns to this topic.)

Progressive employees cheered the baller move; they were proud to work at a socially responsible company. Five-star reviews on Glassdoor were common.[12]

A few years later, a controversial project would test the strength of that bond. As Simone Stolzoff writes in his 2023 book *The Good Enough Job*:

> In mid-August 2018, the Kickstarter Trust and Safety team—which is responsible for maintaining civility on the platform—noticed users had flagged a project for promoting violence. This was relatively common; anyone with a Kickstarter account could flag a project for the Trust and Safety team to review. The project in question was called Always Punch Nazis, a tongue-in-cheek comic

book about the United States's battle against racism, fea-
turing a team of superheroes who, you guessed it, punch
Nazis.[13] The comic was clearly satirical, its pages bursting
with all the over-the-top *pows* and *fwoomps* you might
expect from a graphic novel.

The project's inflammatory nature—and management's handling of it—cracked the foundation. Further incidents would exacerbate the fissure.

Tech companies can't stand still; those that fail to innovate
risk irrelevance or obsolescence. (Hello, Yahoo! and RIM.) To
this end, Kickstarter developed Drip, a Patreon-esque tool that
let project creators start subscriptions and generate recurring
revenue streams.

In 2018, Kickstarter management unilaterally and unexpect-
edly killed Drip—a decision that rankled workers. As employee
Camilla Zhang told *Wired* in May 2020, euthanizing it "came out
of the blue with no consultation" of the very employees who built it
and the creators who had adopted it. "It seemed to be at the whim
of one person to just make a blanket decision," she added.[14]

These types of unilateral management decisions weren't exactly
uncommon in 2018. In fact, they were par for the course and still
are today. Kickstarter, though, was different. Its familial culture
had long been an asset, but it rapidly became a liability. (Newsflash:
family members occasionally bicker.) Friends became enemies. A
bunch of employees attempted to form a union. Management fired
some of them, prompting claims of union-busting.[15] The drama
played out publicly on traditional and social media outlets. No
shocker there.

Fast-forward to February 18, 2020. Kickstarter employees became the first white-collar technology workforce to unionize in US history.[16] Rather than continue fighting, the company's new CEO formally recognized Kickstarter United.

Workers 2, employers 0.

Kickstarter's execs won't be the only ones sitting at a bargaining table. At least they can take solace in that fact. Workers at Starbucks, Apple, Trader Joe's, and the fervently anti-union Amazon voted for collective representation in 2022. However, whether or not each union takes root is an open question. Deep-pocketed corporations typically try to run out the clock on union recognition and collective bargaining.

These examples reflect an overarching trend: US approval of unions has reached its highest point since 1965. In August 2022, a Gallup poll revealed that 71 percent of Americans viewed unions favorably.[17]

Employee empowerment is manifesting itself in a variety of ways. Workers intent on sticking it to the man need not rely on walkouts and unionization campaigns. They have a few other arrows in their quivers.

Additional Signs of Employee Empowerment

Google and Kickstarter are hardly the only companies whose workforces are posing unprecedented conundrums for their management teams. Employees are flexing their muscles in a variety of ways. Walking out and threatening to unionize are just two of them.

Employee Ambition Plunges (aka, Quiet Quitting)

Sumithra Jagannath is the president of ZED Digital, a company that manufactures digital ticket scanners. As she told the *Wall*

Street Journal in late 2022, "The passion that we used to see in work is lower now, and you find it in fewer people—at least in the last two years."[18]

Jagannath is referring to *quiet quitting*—a term you've no doubt heard. Writing for HBR, Jack Zenger and Joseph Folkman describe it as follows:

> Every employee, every workday, makes a decision: Are they only willing to do the minimum work necessary to keep their job? Or are they willing to put more of their energy and effort into their work?
>
> In the last few weeks, many of those who choose the former have self-identified as "quiet quitters." They reject the idea that work should be a central focus of their life. They resist the expectation of giving their all or putting in extra hours. They say "no" to requests to go beyond what they think should be expected of a person in their position.[19]

When I spoke to Jagannath over Zoom in January 2023, she explained how the shortage of qualified, experienced American applicants had forced her to look overseas to fill critical positions.

To be sure, this phenomenon isn't new. Its name and intensity, however, certainly are.

In November 2022, Qualtrics surveyed more than three thousand American workers and managers.[20] Figure 1.3 displays some of its most relevant results.

Not all quitting is quiet—and it hasn't been for a while now. The US Bureau of Labor Statistics reports that the average tenure at an employer dropped nearly 10 percent in 2020 compared to 2010.[21]

Worker Drive Is Waning

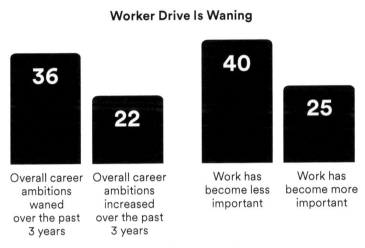

Figure 1.3: Worker Drive Is Waning, Source: Qualtrics

Depending on your politics, you may dismiss the rise of employee empowerment, activism, and voluntary attrition as the actions of spoiled, woke, snowflake American millennials. Make no mistake, though. The trend is gaining traction across the globe.

Chinese Youth Rejects 996

China is home to the extreme work culture called *996*. It's not uncommon for people in the tech and food delivery industries to work 9 a.m. to 9 p.m. six days per week *at a minimum.* Ouch.

In February 2022, a young employee at a Chinese streaming company worked himself to death. Sadly, it wasn't the first tragedy of its type and probably won't be the last. The latest fatality "reignited the debate about China's grueling '996 work culture' in the tech industry."[22]

Young Chinese are embracing the *touching fish movement.* (The term is a play on the proverb, "Muddy waters make it

> easy to catch fish." That is, one can personally benefit from a
> crisis or chaotic period.)
>   Now more people are doing the bare minimum. They're
> explicitly rejecting working unhealthy hours for what they
> perceive to be little gain. Like a good chunk of their American
> millennial counterparts, they're skeptical of the future. When
> you don't see the same opportunities for upward mobility
> afforded to your parents, why bother busting your ass?

Ghosting

At least the quiet quitters who show up do a modicum of work.
A related trend over the past few years has been ghosting, a practice that has spilled over from the online dating world. Current
and future employees who have accepted offers are suddenly and
without explanation cutting off all communication with their current and would-be employers.

One March 2022 survey found that "a whopping 84 percent of
job seekers have ghosted their employer or potential employer in
the past 18 months."[23] As Sinem Buber, lead economist at job site
ZipRecruiter, told *Fast Company*, "They don't think twice about
burning bridges."[24]

Brass tacks: job abandonment is no longer the sole purview
of teenagers who tire of slinging Bang-Bang Chicken at their local Cheesecake Factory. Recruiters report plenty of ghosting for
white-collar jobs as well.

And that's not the only professional norm that has recently
eroded or disappeared.

Tapping Out

Before the pandemic, tens of millions of Americans suffered from mental health issues in the workplace. Many, however, remained silent to avoid their stigma. COVID changed the equation. It intensified both the extent of the problem and the need for organizations to respond to it.

In October 2022, the US Surgeon General reported that 76 percent of American workers reported experiencing at least one symptom of a mental health condition, such as anxiety and depression, in the past year. This number represented an increase of 17 percentage points in just two years.[25] Figure 1.4 shows this disturbing visual.

**US Workers Experiencing
at Least One Mental Health Condition**

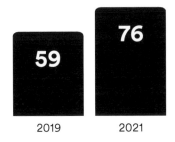

Figure 1.4: US Workers Experiencing at Least One Mental Health Condition. Source: US Surgeon General

This alarming statistic starts to make sense when viewed against a backdrop of the following unsettling events:

- The massive daily uncertainty of living through a pandemic.
- A level of US political polarization not seen since the Civil War.
- The overturning of *Roe v. Wade*.

- The sudden, typically chaotic shift to remote work.
- Revelations of predatory sexual behavior about Harvey Weinstein and prominent male executives.
- The tragic killings of George Floyd and Tyre Nichols.
- The explosion of hate crimes.
- Widespread school shootings and school closings.
- Russia invading Ukraine.
- Disruptions to the supply chain and resultant product shortages.
- Exacerbating climate change and global warming.

Perhaps no single visual summed up the state of the world better than the poster for the 2022 season of Jon Oliver's HBO show *Last Week Tonight*. The exasperated host sits next to a smoking globe with his hands covering his eyes.*

And this distressing list isn't remotely comprehensive. Revisiting Figure 1.4, how did anyone *not* suffer from a mental health issue over the past few years?

Employees are more frequently asking for leaves of absence.[26] Burnout is the most common reason that people are quitting their jobs. A September 2021 survey found that 40 percent of respondents listed it as their primary reason for changing jobs.[27] A recent example underscores the point.

New Zealand Prime Minister Jacinda Ardern resigned in January 2023 because she "no longer had enough in the tank" to do the job.[28] People on social media applauded her honesty and courage because they could relate. A decade ago, I suspect that no PM would have publicly cited burnout.

---

* View it at https://tinyurl.com/9oliver-ps.

In the past, managers who granted fried employees the occasional mental health day generally earned their appreciation. Over the past three years, stressed workers have steadily come to the realization that a single day off won't make everything better anymore. Prior to the pandemic, they were more likely to power through.

What about the workers of the future? Will they be more docile and less entitled? I have my doubts.

Entitlement on Steroids

Organic chemistry isn't for the faint of heart. Your typical university class on the subject has historically been challenging by design. Desirable difficulty is a worthy virtue of the college experience in general, but that goes double in the case of future doctors. After all, society shouldn't carelessly mint its physicians and surgeons.

In the spring of 2022, dozens of NYU students were failing Dr. Maitland Jones's organic chemistry class. Rather than buckle down and study harder, nearly one-quarter of the class sadly did what some of their colleagues have recently done:

> 82 of his 350 students signed a petition against him. Students said the high-stakes course—notorious for ending many a dream of medical school—was too hard, blaming Dr. Jones for their poor test scores.[29]

In August 2022, before the start of the new academic year, the university abruptly dismissed Dr. Jones. In the words of the former head of the chemistry department, James W. Canary, the good doctor:

hasn't changed his style or methods in a good many years. The students have changed, though, and they were asking for and expecting more support from the faculty when they're struggling.[30]

As a recovering college prof myself, I unabashedly side with Dr. Jones. Students are products, not customers—or, if you like, they're *future* customers. A decade from now, they should be grateful that their professors held them accountable. (There. Rant over.)

For our purposes, here's the main point: these students will eventually enter the workforce with an unprecedented sense of entitlement that their future bosses will need to manage. (Yes, writing that sentence made me feel like a curmudgeon.)

Why Workers Are Flexing Their Muscles

At this point, it's instructive to ask a fundamental question: why are workers suddenly and so forcefully flexing their muscles?

In short, because they can. The longer answer, of course, requires some time to unpack.

Financial Pressures Ease

A majority of Americans have long lived paycheck to paycheck. At any given point, the financial services company LendingClub estimates the number to be roughly three in five.[31] As layoffs spiked in April 2020 and a cloud of uncertainty loomed over the economy, how would we respond?

Months of lockdown caused us to involuntarily reduce our discretionary expenses. We ceased taking vacations, dining out, and attending sporting events and concerts. Watching Gary Gulman and Taylor Tomlinson on Netflix costs less than buying tickets to their stand-up shows, paying for parking, and ordering a few drinks.

We curtailed our expenses while our income often *increased.* Armed with government stimulus checks, millions of people—particularly Americans—now found themselves in unique positions with modest savings.

States offered more generous unemployment benefits than normal. As a result, claims in April 2020 skyrocketed, causing antiquated state websites and systems to collapse.[32]

Thanks to stimulus checks, government assistance, and reduced outlays, the recently furloughed were able to manage their periods of joblessness effectively. When it came to looking for proper jobs, people were choosier than normal. The National Bureau of Economic Research found that "expanded benefits slowed workers' return to the labor market and prolonged unemployment spells during the summer of 2021."[33]

The Existential Questions of COVID-19

Without the same economic pressure, tens of millions reassessed their stations in life. They asked big, hairy questions, such as:

- Why am I risking my life for minimum wage?
- Is it time that I finally left my job or changed careers?
- Should I continue to tolerate my toxic work environment, boss, or colleagues?
- If I don't hang my own shingle now, will I ever get up the nerve?
- What if I got out of the rat race altogether?

Academics, economists, management gurus, and journalists labeled the ensuing period the *Great Resignation*, the *Great Reset*, and the *Great Reevaluation*. Regardless of its moniker, the result is indisputable: a dramatic labor market shift that is still confounding employers and economists. (We'll return to this subject later in the chapter.)

#MeToo and #BLM Redefine Acceptable Workplace Conduct

In the past, a great deal of racist, misogynist, and generally inappropriate behavior took place in the workplace. We regularly looked the other way because we needed a paycheck, or the offending employee or team delivered results. Case in point: Andy Rubin, referenced earlier in this chapter.

Like it or not, social mores have changed—and probably forever. Call it *cancel culture* if you want, but we're less willing to accept this behavior. As a society, we've started drawing lines. In all sorts of ways, consumers and workers are voting with their wallets, pocketbooks, and feet.

For example, we used to pooh-pooh allegations of domestic violence. Now charges of hitting your wife or girlfriend—not convictions, mind you—swiftly result in termination. This goes double if you represent a highly visible organization, such as the coach of a college team.[34]

Let's look at the owners of two prominent American sports franchises:

- Daniel Snyder of the NFL's Washington Commanders.
- Robert Sarver of the NBA's Phoenix Suns and the WNBA's Mercury.

In both cases, multiple investigations found that these owners created toxic work cultures. (A seventy-nine-page congressional report details Snyder's brazen malfeasance.[35]) Their respective league commissioners responded by encouraging them to exit stage left. Each demurred.

Professional wrestling doesn't qualify as a *sport*. Common euphemisms for it include *choreographed athletic theater* and *sports entertainment*. Semantic distinctions aside, its most prominent public figure has shown that he's anything but a saint. In mid-2022, WWE chief Vince McMahon had to step away amid reports that he paid a "total of $12 million to four women to quiet sexual misconduct allegations."[36] In January 2023, McMahon announced his imminent plans to return to facilitate the sale of his company.

Sarver sold his franchises to United Wholesale Mortgage CEO Mat Ishbia for $4 billion. By the time you read these words, I suspect that Snyder and McMahon will have joined Sarver in formally and permanently relinquishing their respective roles. Don't throw them pity parties, though. The troika will have profited immensely from their forced departures. They will leave rich, free men. In other words, they'll probably avoid the fates of some of their billionaire counterparts who played fast and loose with the rules.

Streaming Shines a Spotlight on Bad Bosses

In November 2022, a judge sentenced Theranos founder and CEO Elizabeth Holmes to eleven years in prison after jurors found her guilty of four counts of fraud. Trevor Milton held the same position at the electric vehicle startup Nikola. Despite his protestations, he's heading to the clink for similar crimes.[37]

After years of erratic and irresponsible behavior, WeWork's Adam Neumann and Uber's Travis Kalanick also fell from glory. As much as Neumann and Kalanick want to scrub their ignominious behavior and exits from the internet, they can't. In each case, millions know why they fell from grace—and not because they watched CNBC, followed the business press, or read any of the excellent tell-alls.

Streaming exploded during lockdown. Global subscriptions surpassed the one-billion mark for the first time.[38] The gaudy number excluded shared passwords and accounts, although Netflix and others have started cracking down on the practice.[39]

Eager for compelling content, Apple, Netflix, Hulu, and others raced to tell Shakespearean business stories:

- *The Dropout* stars as the sociopathic CEO. Her performance garnered a Primetime Emmy Award for Outstanding Lead Actress in a Limited or Anthology Series or Movie.
- *Dopesick* reveals the carnage that Richard Sackler caused. I'll never understand how Purdue Pharma's former Oxycontin king isn't wearing an orange jumpsuit.
- Showtime's *Super Pumped* details Kalanick's spectacular rise and fall. *WeCrashed* on AppleTV+ details how Neumann crashed and burned.
- *Madoff: The Monster of Wall Street* hit Netflix in early 2023. Madoff's story was hardly new, and he died in 2021. The streaming giant no doubt saw the success of similar shows before greenlighting this cautionary four-part series.

I'd be stupefied if development and negotiations aren't already underway to bring Sam Bankman-Fried to your living room. The founder of the cryptocurrency exchange FTX faces a lifetime in prison for his Madoff-level fraud.

As the author of a bunch of books, I know the importance of the written word. Still, even award-winning business reporters have to concede that exceptional documentaries, TV series, and movies evoke more visceral reactions than stories do.* Oh, and screens usually reach more viewers than texts do these days. American book readership has steadily declined over the past two decades. Today, one in six reads precisely zero each year.[40]

Millions of people watched the accounts of Holmes, Sackler, Neumann, Kalanick, and Madoff in varying degrees of horror. No, our CEO is probably not corrupt or evil. Still, how could these shows *not* affect how many of us view the rich bigwigs who sit in corner offices and demand that we return to the office full-time?

How Bosses Are Responding

Since this is a book about forces, let's explore a few of the ways that employers are countering their newly empowered workforces.

Go, Elon!

Employers may have had to tolerate work from home (WFH) and increasing employee empowerment during the Great Resignation. That doesn't mean, though, that they'll swallow their pride forever. Executives have started putting down their feet—and one, in particular, hasn't been too subtle about it.

Yep, it's time to discuss Elon Musk, Twitter, and bossism.

---

* Although I love Stephen King's novel *Misery*, it doesn't convey the brutality of its most iconic scene in the same way that the movie does.

The polarizing head of SpaceX, Tesla, and now the embattled social network is nothing if not newsworthy. Writing for the *New York Times* in December 2022, Kevin Roose describes how business leaders are rooting for the unhinged chief twit to succeed. It's worth quoting at length:

> But while some tech CEOs might blame a sleeper cell of gender-studies majors for their problems, many of Mr. Musk's elite fans adhere to a more straightforward, business-school kind of bossism. They admire him for ruling Twitter with an iron fist and making the kinds of moves that tech executives have resisted for fear of alienating workers—cutting jobs, stripping away perks, punishing internal dissenters, resisting diversity and inclusion efforts, and forcing employees back to the office.
>
> These bossists* believe that for the past decade or so, a booming tech industry and a talent shortage forced many CEOs to make unreasonable concessions. They spoiled workers with perks like lavish meals and kombucha on tap. They agreed to use workplace chat apps like Slack, which flattened office hierarchies and gave junior workers a way to directly challenge leadership. They bent over backward to give in to worker demands—DEI† workshops, flexible remote work policies, company wellness days— to keep them happy and prevent them from jumping ship to a competitor.[41]

---

* Interestingly, the term *baasskap* roughly translates to *boss-ship* or *boss-hood*. It's also linked with South Africa and apartheid.

† Short for *diversity, equity, and inclusion.*

Forget free lunches and office snacks. Those are distant memories. The remaining Twitter employees would do well to pack their own toilet paper before heading to the office. No, I'm not exaggerating or joking.[42]

Hundreds of employees opted to resign in the wake of Musk's demand that they embrace an "extremely hardcore" Twitter when he took over the company.[43] Many proudly did so on Twitter itself. Unfortunately, some employees will have to stomach Musk's antics. Most notably, immigrants on H-1B visas who find themselves out of work face deportation if they can't land new jobs within 60 days.

The Anti-Elons: The Progressive CEOs Who Get It

Only the most oblivious founders and executives fail to realize that COVID-19 fundamentally and permanently altered our relationship with work. Although not everyone understands that putting the genie back in the bottle is futile, plenty do.

These folks are embracing remote and hybrid work, not to mention the technologies discussed in this book.

Are there obstacles? Sure. Figuring out the new normal isn't easy. It's not like following a tried-and-true playbook to open a new Chipotle or Arby's. Challenges aside, they've decided that the juice of adapting is more than worth its squeeze. Specifically, promulgating pro-employee policies allows firms to lure top talent from their old-school competitors. It's a unique opportunity with the potential to keep paying dividends.

Providing Additional Resources

Confronted with burned-out employees, most large employers have, to their credit, recognized that they needed to do more than simply provide a paycheck. They stepped up to the plate in different ways. Exhibit A: by 2022, roughly 90 percent of Fortune 500 companies have created different employee resource groups.[44] Some smaller firms subsequently have followed suit.

Adopting New Technologies

As we'll see in upcoming chapters, employers are doing more than merely issuing ultimatums and mandates. They're deploying emerging technologies to redress this power imbalance once and for all.

Understanding the Not-So-Subtle Threat of Mass Layoffs

As 2022 concluded, Amazon, Salesforce, Google, Meta, and others made headlines. In the tech sector alone, more than 150,000 people lost their jobs in 2022—exceeding the total in the prior two years combined.[45] The trend has continued into the new year. Microsoft shredded ten thousand employees in January 2023.[46] (Blame overly ambitious growth expectations and resultant overhiring.) Plenty of non-tech CEOs and company presidents followed suit and cut back as they headed toward uncertain economic times.

Surely, these public mass firings would finally swing the pendulum back to management, right? Writing for the *Wall Street Journal* in February 2023, Chip Cutter and Theo Francis declared, "The bosses are back in charge."[47]

I'm no Nostradamus, but I wouldn't go nearly that far.

The next section describes why bosses won't get all their prepandemic mojo back anytime soon.

Why Empowered Employees Are Here to Stay

Before continuing, a brief disclaimer is in order. The labor market is a complex beast. Conflicting data and signals are flummoxing economists. Making accurate macroeconomic predictions has never been easy, and forecasting the future today is even trickier than usual. The economy *may* be barreling toward a recession, but historically we haven't seen downturns accompanied by low unemployment.

The Incredible Shrinking Labor Supply

On November 30, 2022, the Bureau of Labor Statistics released its highly anticipated Job Openings and Labor Turnover Survey. Among its most interesting findings:

- The US had 10.33 million vacancies for the month. This number represented a decline of 353,000 from September of 760,000 compared to the same period last year.
- The unemployment rate remained historically low at 3.7 percent.
- There were 1.7 job openings per available worker for the month, down from a 2-to-1 ratio in August.[48]

It's fair to classify the current labor market as *imbalanced*. Broadly speaking, more jobs are available than people to fill them. And there's no quick fix. The problem is structural, making its solution neither fast nor simple.

Millions Have Bowed Out of the Labor Market

It's a tough circle to square, but remember this vital point: in the US, the national unemployment rate only reflects people *actively* looking for jobs. In the parlance of the US Bureau of Labor

Statistics, "all persons who are without jobs and are actively seeking and available to work are included among the unemployed."[49] More succinctly, the official numbers exclude those who have bowed out of the labor force.

It's a mistake to dismiss that group as trivial.

Seventy years ago, 2 percent of American men aged twenty-five to fifty-four didn't work. Today, that number has ballooned to 11 percent.[50] And the US is no outlier. In the United Kingdom, the statistic is almost identical: 10 percent.[51]

Compared to previous decades, fewer people are looking for jobs. You don't have to be Milton Friedman or John Maynard Keynes to recognize how a reduction in the labor force will affect the economy. Will it continue?

Yes.

From WWII to 2019, the US labor force grew at an annualized rate of 1 percent.[52] In September 2022, the Bureau of Labor Statistics projected less than half that annual rate from 2021 to 2031.[53] As Patrick Coate of the National Council on Compensation Insurance put it, "Labor supply issues are likely to persist as workforce demographics indicate slow labor force growth over the next decade."[54]

Layoffs Revisited

Layoffs from Amazon, Microsoft, and other bellwethers make headlines and scare us, but they have masked a larger trend: since the pandemic began, the US has *added* far more jobs than it has lost.

Small business growth over the past three years has been phenomenal. It has driven the historically strong labor market. Since

February 2020, firms with fewer than 250 employees have hired 3.67 million *more* people than they've lost.[55] That number starkly contrasts with larger businesses that employ 250 individuals or more. As a whole, the latter group has trimmed 800,000 net jobs during this period.

US Immigration

Thanks to COVID-19 and the policies of the previous US administration, immigration to the US sharply declined from 2017 to 2022.[56] As of December 2022, "immigrants in the United States are becoming citizens in numbers not seen for more than a decade."[57] Whether this trend continues is an open question that largely hinges upon who wins the presidential election in 2024.

The Declining US Birth Rate

As of this writing, employers are struggling to fill open jobs. To be fair, a more welcoming immigration policy can quickly provide much needed talent and relief. One long-term trend, however, worries employers, chambers of commerce, think tanks, and other industry trade groups: Americans are procreating less. In 2020, the US general fertility rate dropped 15.9 percent from its average over the decade ending in 2010. Ten states saw declines greater than 20 percent.[58]

In fairness, Japan,[59] France,[60] and other industrialized countries are experiencing the same issue—and it began well before COVID-19.

Fewer births mean fewer workers. One culprit in the US: student loan debt. It often represents a significant hurdle for would-be mothers in the prime of their child-bearing years.[61]

Economic Necessity, Inflation, and Side Hustles

Yes, copious folks are quietly quitting, refusing to go the extra mile for their employers, and even dropping out of the workforce altogether. Somewhat paradoxically, though, we're looking for supplemental sources of income.

In October 2022, technology company Qualtrics surveyed more than one thousand American adults with full-time jobs. Nearly four in ten have looked for a side hustle, and another 14 percent plan to do so.[62]

Individual circumstances vary, but inflation (discussed much more in Chapter 3) is unsurprisingly the main culprit. Nearly seven in ten respondents said as much. In the words of Matt Schulz, LendingTree's chief credit analyst:

> And now that inflation has gone wild, more and more people have embraced side hustles out of necessity. Life is really expensive today and many people need that extra side hustle income to make ends meet or to provide themselves with a little bit of financial wiggle room.[63]

Millions of folks need to find supplemental income to rebuild their eroded purchasing power. The problem is particularly acute for middle-class, non-managerial, and exempt employees who don't qualify for overtime pay under current labor laws.

The End of Non-Competes?

Another traditional way that employers have kept senior-level employees in check involves non-compete agreements. In a nutshell, organizations have used NCAs as cudgels for decades. They've legally restricted current or former employees from working for competitors.[64] Sometimes the period lasts two years after the worker's employment ends.[65]

In January 2023, the Federal Trade Commission proposed a rule forbidding companies from subjecting workers to NCAs.[66] Lina Khan is the agency's current chair and loudly expressed her beliefs in a compelling *New York Times* op-ed, saying NCAs depress wages and kill innovation.[67]

Again, score another victory for the empowered employee.

Tying It All Together

Where does this leave us?

Employee empowerment may wane a bit. As a group, it's hard to envision workers getting much more demanding. (The level had nowhere to go but down.) Also, a father of three is unlikely to tell his boss that he's sticking with remote work forty-eight hours after she just laid off half of his colleagues.

That drop, however, will be a temporary blip on an otherwise uninterrupted upward trajectory from prior decades. Workers are holding their best cards in years, and they know it. In other words, more emboldened employees are here to stay. They're flexing their muscles in a variety of ways, especially regarding where they'll work.

Let location serve as the starting point for the next chapter.

Key Points

- Google paid an influential executive an obscene amount of money to leave. Four years later, employee unrest erupted.
- Years of employee-management goodwill at Kickstarter swiftly evaporated.
- Making sense of the current labor market is vexing the smartest forecasters.

- As the rise in ghosting illustrates, burning professional bridges no longer serves as the same deterrent as it once did.
- Don't expect the return of the largely silent and compliant workforce from previous decades. Powerful labor market forces and structural issues make curbing employee empowerment unlikely, at least in the short term.

CHAPTER 2

Physical Dispersion

The war over where we work is over. Deal with it.

"I am never going back."
—ROBERT DE NIRO AS NEIL MCCAULEY, *HEAT*

If you're a coder, you'd be hard-pressed to find a better milieu than Silicon Valley, California. Yeah, the traffic sucks, the air quality can be dangerous, and the rents are insane. But you've got your pick of the employment litter. The Valley is home to some of the world's most iconic firms: Google, Dropbox, Apple, Meta, Cisco, eBay, Intel, Uber, LinkedIn, Adobe, Netflix, and PayPal—just to name a few.

With so much talent so close by, these companies frequently try to poach each other's employees. Preventing coveted peeps from going across the street sometimes necessitates doling out six-figure retention bonuses and lush stock-option packages.[1]

For workers with these special sets of skills, the threat of defection is neither exaggerated nor terribly new. In 2009, Steve Jobs famously found himself in hot water after demanding that then-Google CEO Eric Schmidt stop recruiting Apple engineers.[2] Schmidt immediately agreed to cease the practice and fire the recruiter in question, but that didn't make Jobs's request legal. Today it would be accurate to call Silicon Valley's tech community *clubby*, although *incestuous* might be a better word.

So, when a prominent techie leaves one tech giant for another, it hardly qualifies as news—unless, of course, it's Ian Goodfellow.

According to Goodfellow's LinkedIn profile,[3] he began working at Apple as its director of machine learning in its Special Projects Group in March 2019. (Don't let the clunkiness of the title fool you. Machine learning is a white-hot subset of artificial intelligence; expert practitioners can essentially write their own tickets.) By all accounts, Goodfellow was relatively happy in that role. He enjoyed his full-time, remote schedule. His mood changed, though, in April 2022 after his employer announced its return-to-work plan.

Figure 2.1 shows a related tweet from Zoë Schiffer of The Verge.

One can hardly fault Apple for wanting its employees to, you know, occasionally show up at its $5 billion "space-age wonderplex designed by Steve Jobs."[4] Even for Apple, that's a decent amount of cheddar.

Figure 2.1: Tweet From Zoë Schiffer of The Verge, Source: Twitter

But Goodfellow wasn't interested in returning to the office. With his skillset, pedigree, and home in the Bay Area, he knew that he wouldn't have to send out a slew of resumes if he decided to make a move. A few weeks after tendering his resignation, he started a plum gig as a research scientist at DeepMind, a British artificial intelligence laboratory that Google gobbled up in 2014. I'd be amazed if Goodfellow didn't broach his location preferences during interviews.

To recap, one of the world's most respected and valuable companies changed its return-to-office (RTO) policy, promptly causing it to lose a critical employee to one of its fiercest rivals. Apple will be fine, of course; its market cap hovers around $2 trillion as of this writing. But what if hundreds or thousands of its in-demand employees follow suit?

WFH: The Job Perk Has Become a Requirement

Let's rewind to April 2020.

COVID-19 could have turned out to be a minor annoyance that lasted a few weeks to a month. Many folks believed as much in March 2020. As I wrote in *Project Management in the Hybrid Workplace* a year ago:

> If this scenario had played out, workers would have viewed the work-from-home (WFH) period as the equivalent of a few snow days or a *workation*. For a short, joyous time, they would have taken a brief respite from the normal drudgery of putting their faces on, commuting to the office, enduring obnoxious colleagues, and working in environments that rarely compared to the comforts of their homes. When the dust finally settled, I suspect that most employees would have returned to the office, if somewhat grudgingly.

Of course, a far different scenario played out. Untold millions of people have now been able to work in a remote or hybrid fashion for the better part of three years. They've dramatically reduced commuting time, picked up new hobbies, spent more time with family and friends, and finally gained some work-life balance.

For many, remote/hybrid work is no longer a perk; it's become a hill on which they're willing to die. They won't willingly give it back—and a veritable trove of data supports that assertion.

Software developers and other techies are hardly alone in wanting to maintain remote and hybrid work arrangements. In December 2022, the compensation software vendor Payscale released its End-of-Year Hot Jobs Report. Look under the heading "Jobs people are most likely to quit," and you'll find the following critical—if clunky—sentence:

Topping the list are Senior Customer Service Represen-
tatives, which have seen decent salary growth but where
the work is stressful and can be unrewarding depending
on how employees and customers are treated and valued,
and where employees are also being asked to return to
office environments.[5]

Note the curious use of the word *asked* in that long sentence. As a former customer service rep, I can assure you: management typically doesn't *ask* entry-level, nonexempt folks to do anything. *Tell* is the more apropos verb.

In its 2022 State of Remote Work Survey, Buffer asked respondents, "Would you recommend remote work to others?" Only 3 percent didn't.

Consider the results of a November 2022 survey of one thousand remote workers by Reli Exchange, an insurance tech company. Seventy-five percent of employers had instructed staff to return to onsite work at least part of the time. In 26 percent of these cases, respondents claimed to have disobeyed these mandates. What's more, these folks were willing to live with the consequences. If the decision meant getting fired, then so be it.[6] Interestingly, younger Gen Xers and older millennials were the least likely to comply with return-to-office orders.

The career website Zety produced similar results in its October 2022 survey. The company surveyed over a thousand US workers about their work expectations for the new year. Three in five said they'd rather quit their job than return to their desks every day.[7]

These results may leave you skeptical. When push comes to shove, will *all* of these folks quit rather than report to the office five days per week?

The short answer is *no*. Some people are bluffing and, as the economy invariably worsens, others will bite their belts—at least for the time being. Expect reluctant employees to soon start poking around for jobs that grant them the flexibility to which they've become accustomed.

As Abha Bhattarai wrote for the *Washington Post* in November 2022:

> Fifty percent of job applications submitted on LinkedIn are for work-from-home positions, which make up just 15 percent of listings, according to a recent report from the jobs site.[8]

Figure 2.2 shows this stark imbalance.

Supply and Demand Collide— Remote Jobs Posted on LinkedIn

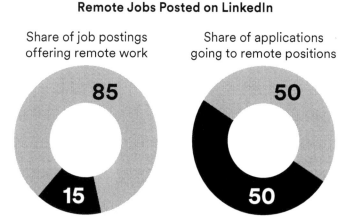

Share of job postings offering remote work

85

15

Share of applications going to remote positions

50

50

Figure 2.2: Supply and Demand Collide—Remote Jobs Posted on LinkedIn
Source: LinkedIn

Before concluding this section, remember that *when* we work matters just about as much as *where*. Three-quarters of respondents in the Zety survey also wanted flexibility in setting their own hours.

If anything, that last number may understate worker sentiment. Future Forum is a consortium that helps companies navigate the new world of work. Figure 2.3 displays a particularly relevant finding from its Fall 2022 Pulse Survey.[9]

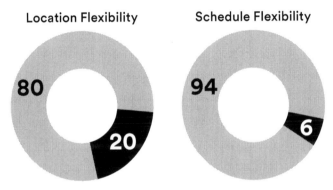

American Workers Oppose Reverting to Pre-COVID Work Conditions

Percent of desk-based workers who want ...

Location Flexibility   **Schedule Flexibility**

Figure 2.3: American Workers Oppose Reverting to Pre-COVID Work Conditions
Sources: Future Forum Pulse and Wave 8, August 2022

No matter how compelling or consistent, charts, statistics, and surveys may not resonate with you to the same extent as stories. As a species, stories illustrate points and help us make sense of the world. That's why we remember them.

Hundreds of Virginia state employees had been working remotely since the start of the COVID-19 pandemic. In July 2022, Governor Glenn Youngkin decided to quickly end the policy. To be fair, his new edict did allow "employees to submit applications to work remotely but with various approval processes depending on the number of days per week requested."[10]

You can probably guess what happened.

Over three hundred people in five state agencies promptly resigned. Good luck backfilling those positions with talented folks, not that Youngkin cares either way.

Across the globe in India, WhiteHat Jr, a company that produces online classes, experienced a similar fate. In March 2022, its management asked employees to return to offices in Mumbai, Bengaluru, and Gurugram within a month. More than eight hundred employees collectively opted to walk rather than return to the office.[11]

Employee Dispersion Is Here to Stay

As the previous section manifests, rank-and-file employees have grown to love the notions of remote and hybrid work. The sentiments are practically unanimous. Managers, though, remain less enthused about WFH:

- A July 2021 survey from the Society for Human Resource Management revealed that 72 percent of the latter "prefer all of their subordinates to be working in the office."[12]
- At the end of 2021, Northeastern University found that more than half of C-suite executives were concerned about their workforce's ability to be creative and innovative in a primarily remote work environment.[13]

Executives and managers who insist upon a full-time return to the office will ultimately lose this battle. (Plenty of people have argued that the war is already over.) For a bevy of reasons, dispersed and distributed workforces will persevere; hybrid won't go the way of the dodo.

The Current Expectations Gap Is Already Small

Nick Bloom is a Stanford economics professor who studies work-from-home topics. His WFH research team reported that, as of January 2023, "Workers say they want to work from home for 2.8 days on average, versus employers planning to allow 2.3 days remote."[14] Put differently, there's a zone of possible agreement.

Workers Freakin' Love It

Employees rightly view the ability to work from home as a godsend. The National Bureau of Economic Research in January 2023 reported that, in 2021 and 2022, workers saved worldwide an average of 72 minutes per day by not having to commute. US workers reclaimed nearly an hour of their daily lives. In China, that number is a mind-boggling 102 minutes.[15]

The paper's authors argue that these impressive numbers *understate* the true value of working from home. Workers accrue additional benefits by:

- Saving money on gas, tolls, and train or bus fares.
- Spending less time putting their faces on.
- Feeling a greater sense of autonomy over how they spend their time.

It's hard to overestimate how transformative even a few days of weekly remote work can be. Employees have "experienced new levels of fulfillment working from home," says Dr. Caitlin Duffy, research director at the advisor firm Gartner. "It has been hard for companies to justify walking that back."[16]

Your Competitors Are Doing It

Allow me to state the obvious: when most of your competitors are offering a perk that employees universally love, it's harder to deny it. That's especially true in tight labor markets.

Money Matters

An August 2021 GoodHire study found that workers were willing to put their money where their mouths were. To keep working remotely, survey respondents had this to say:

- Sixty-one percent would accept less compensation.
- Seventy percent would forfeit benefits like health insurance, retirement accounts, and paid time off. [17]

But the savings don't stop there. Organizations can reduce their real estate costs, sometimes by considerable amounts. (Chapter 9 will revisit this topic.)

We're Not Novices Anymore

Go back to the early days of the pandemic. In April and early May of 2020, odds are that you, your colleagues, and your employer's IT department struggled with basic blocking and tackling. Did your first few Zoom meetings go smoothly? Memes and stories of Zoom gaffes were popular fodder on social media. I detailed some of the most interesting ones in *Zoom For Dummies*.

It's understandable. As Figure 2.4 shows, Zoom's growth in early 2020 was stratospheric.

We still make occasional mistakes. Three years into the new normal, though, most of us have figured out how to work more effectively when away from the office. For one, we're better at using Zoom, Slack, Microsoft Teams, and other internal collaboration hubs.

Zoom's User Base Grows 2,900 Percent in Four Months
Daily active users (in millions)

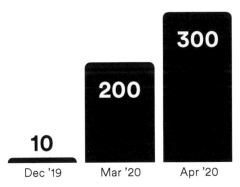

Figure 2.4: Zoom's User Base Grows 2,900 Percent in Four Months
Source: Zoom

Tools aside and more broadly, as Alexandra Samuel and my friend Terri Griffith note in a *Wall Street Journal* opinion piece:

> The hybrid workplace, in other words, isn't a free pass to go backward. Nor is it a free pass to throw out everything that worked before. It's an opportunity to take what we learned during the pandemic and build something new, something better. And the first step in that process is to be honest about what isn't working. And then fix it.[18]

In a word, *yes.*

Reputations Matter

Employers with progressive employment policies hold an advantage over those that demand in-person daily work. Fine. But how do prospective workers know which policies are legit? And can't employers tell their employees and applicants one thing but do another?

Sure. Management can undoubtedly play loose with its actual WFH policies, but the deception is unlikely to work.

Whether it's on Twitter, Snap, or popular work-oriented apps like Blink and Fishbowl, employees talk. The website Glassdoor reports that a full 86 percent of job seekers look at a company's reviews and ratings before deciding where to apply for a job.[19] When companies walk back their remote work policies, affected workers aren't shy about voicing their displeasure.

The Ability to Recruit From a Larger Candidate Pool

Although quit rates have tapered off a bit as of this writing, they're still near historic highs. A hiring manager may *prefer* to hire a quality local candidate for an open position, but can she find one? Maybe not.

A year into the pandemic, the *New York Times* and the *Wall Street Journal* ran extensive pieces on pandemic-induced US migration. From the latter:

> From coast to coast, Americans migrated toward less-dense, more-affordable areas as they sought more space and, in some cases, became untethered by the ability to work from anywhere.[20]

Subsequent research has confirmed those findings. In January 2023, *The Economist* published a piece titled "How Technology Is Redrawing the Boundaries of the Firm." From it:

> Using data from America's Quarterly Census of Employment and Wages, *The Economist* has examined jobs in three sectors particularly compatible with remote work: technology, finance, and professional services. Our analysis finds that such jobs have become far more distributed

across America since the pandemic. Big metropolitan areas have lost out to smaller cities and even the countryside.[21]

Employers may *prefer* to hire local candidates out of habit or comfort. Nevertheless, they may *have* to consider remote or hybrid employees out of necessity. Maybe paying $25,000 or more in relocation costs is the lesser of two evils, but what if that promising new hire doesn't work out? And what if she bolts after a year?

卌 IIII

I could cite more data and research, but you get the point. The era in which all employees descended to the same physical location during the same hours has ended. This shift portends significant changes for traditional offices and other physical locations.

How Does the Postpandemic Workplace Look?

This question has three answers. Before getting to them, though, a little context is in order.

Progressive management teams have already tapped out; they've conceded that a full-blown return to the office won't happen—and shouldn't, for that matter. That realization solves some problems, but it introduces others. Proximity bias is a biggie: leaders *naturally* view workers they can see more favorably than workers they can't.

Now, proximity bias doesn't make us evil; it just makes us human. It also forces leaders to come to terms with its harmful consequences. Here are two stats that should give anyone pause:

- More than two in five managers reported sometimes forgetting about remote workers when assigning tasks.[22]
- Despite being 15 percent more productive on average than their peers, remote workers are promoted less often than their in-person counterparts.[23]

Ouch.

Setting up shop in the postpandemic world requires some forethought and introspection. We need to challenge traditional notions of why workers go to the office. Above all, we must embrace experimentation. It's the antithesis of merely saying, "Playtime's over. Back to work."

Corporate Headquarters Reimagined

Against this backdrop, let's see how three companies thoughtfully redesigned their workspaces.

Cisco Embraces Data and Polygons

Former Cisco Executive Chairman and CEO John Chambers once said that his company made the plumbing behind the internet. Routers, modems, switches, and other types of hardware didn't fit anyone's definition of *sexy*, but email, websites, and Wi-Fi wouldn't work without products like the ones that his company made.

With technology embedded in Cisco's DNA, it should be no surprise that its new Manhattan office is flat-out loaded with the latest tchotchkes. The 54,000-square-foot space at One Penn Plaza in Manhattan serves as both a showcase for its products and its vision for the future of work. (Spoiler alert: it's hybrid.)

The old layout dedicated 70 percent of its space to individual workstations; the other 30 went to group-based collaboration. The revamped one inverts those numbers. Why come into the office when you're primarily going to do individual work?

Sounds great, right? Depending on your point of view, things are about to get a little creepy. (Chapter 8 will return to the subject of unhealthy analytics.)

Cameras are everywhere, and the company knows the current floor occupancy at any given time. Employees' mobile devices and Cisco's wireless access points allow managers to know where all *anonymized* employees and visitors are. (The lack of permanent employee desks and offices makes tracking this data especially important. Workers would be justifiably annoyed if they commuted to the office for a meeting only to find that there's no space for them to hold it.)

Cisco has assigned 1,700 of its employees to this location. It chronically collects 5,000 individual data points at a time. Tech also tracks the number of meeting participants and people in a given room. Sensors also capture air quality, temperature, and humidity.

Before entering the office, employees can view available collaboration and meeting spaces. When an employee taps her fingers on an open space on the large screen, the system holds it for her for four minutes.

As one of the project's designers put it:

> With hybrid here to say, we're seeing so much more emphasis on amenity spaces [and] collaboration spaces. People are coming in to be with other people [to do] the things they can't do when working at home.

Cisco's senior leadership is determined to prevent remote and hybrid workers from becoming second-class citizens. The company calls its approach to combat proximity bias *digital equality*. It starts with simple things, like the shape of conference-room tables. Rectangular ones routinely make it difficult for virtual meeting participants to see others, and vice versa. Figure 2.5 shows the basic geometry of polygons.

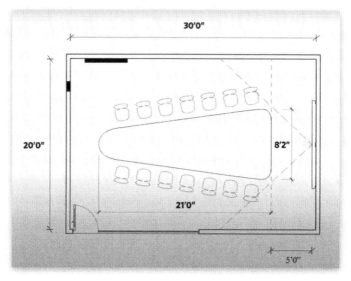

Figure 2.5: Cisco's Redesigned Conference Room, Source: Cisco

Again, I encourage you to watch a video of it yourself.*

LinkedIn Doubles Down on Experimentation

The company completely redesigned its headquarters with hybrid work in mind. The new, far more open layout includes more than—get this—75 different types of seating. It's an astonishing, even radical departure from the company's previous, more traditional configuration.

---

* Watch the video at https://tinyurl.com/14-simon-cisco.

When asked about the overarching philosophy behind the re-
design, Robert Norwood, a principal at NBBJ Design, said:

> We really wanted to do a lot of experimentation because
> we just didn't know. No one had a crystal ball about what
> the future would actually be. We wanted to provide ... as
> many ... spaces as possible.

Standard employee desks, cubicles, and traditional conference
rooms are now flexible areas. The new meeting rooms resemble
living rooms; they're far less formal than their antecedents. Rooms
intelligently include screens and cameras positioned at table
height. The hardware automatically reframes virtual speakers and
lets them easily view their in-person counterparts.

Figure 2.6 shows a photo of the new LinkedIn digs.

Figure 2.6: LinkedIn's Redesigned Headquarters, Photo credit: Eric Laignel

Again, my description and a single photo don't do the remake
justice. Go and watch a YouTube video of it yourself.* You'll find

---

* Watch the video at https://tinyurl.com/14-simon-linkedin.

similarities to Cisco's new HQ, including some similarly shaped conference tables.

Dropbox Makes Bold Moves to Increase Employee Retention

Relatively early in the pandemic, the popular storage service launched Virtual First, a program codifying its employee-friendly work policies. Dropbox expected its peeps to work virtually at least 90 percent of the time. They'd only need to occasionally trek into the office for brainstorming sessions, special educational meetings, and team-bonding activities.

In a related vein, the company reimagined the office—and not by merely conducting a rebranding campaign. As Lisa Ardill of *Silicon Republic* writes:

> Dropbox staff will also have access to new communal spaces called Dropbox Studios. These will be set up "once it's safe to do so" to allow teams to collaborate in person, the company said. Studios will be developed in cities where Dropbox already has offices and a high concentration of employees—Dublin, San Francisco, Seattle, and Austin, to start—and there may be on-demand spaces in other locations. Dropbox Studios will be specifically for collaboration and community-building, and employees will not be able to use them for solo work.[24]

Reread that last sentence.

The move allowed Dropbox to free up a boatload of office space, including 700,000 square feet in downtown San Francisco. It subsequently subleased the space, earning "$14.8 million in rent from its various real estate properties through the third quarter of this year,"[25] according to its November 2022 earnings report.

Part of the savings and new revenue went to employees in the form of annual $7,000 work-at-home stipends. (Yes, *annual.*) Those payments "cover anything from childcare to gym membership to a spiffy new ergonomic desk and chair."[26]

Did it work?

At first, not so much. Turnover exploded; survey data showed that employees loved location- and time-independent work but craved in-person interaction with their colleagues. Chief People Officer Melanie Rosenwasser tweaked Virtual First to encourage real-world team and department meetings.

But then Dropbox's record-high attrition rate fell to the lowest in company history. Moreover, employee engagement scores increased by 12 percent from 2020 to 2022.

Lessons

And these companies are hardly alone in going all-in on the hybrid future of work—and designing their offices accordingly. No one would ever confuse the new digs of Adobe, Samsung, Marriott, and Amazon with their parents' cubicle farms.*

Has each high-tech makeover *eliminated* proximity bias and the other problems inherent in remote and hybrid work? No, that would be overstating things. Here are two better questions to ask:

- Have they significantly improved the experience for remote and hybrid workers?
- Are they setting the stage for future improvements?

The answer to each query is an unequivocal *yes*. Redesigned corporate headquarters are frequently smaller, more modern,

---

* This *Wall Street Journal* series Open Office is worth checking out. See https://tinyurl.com/14-wsj-oo-simon.

more configurable, and—thanks to new tech—far more accessible and equitable to remote and hybrid workers.

But the changes to HQ go far beyond removing cubicles and applying a fresh coat of paint. There's another, arguably more important dimension to dispersion.

Working Neither at Home Nor in the Main Office

Smaller headquarters typically can't accommodate all of an organization's local employees, never mind the job applicants, partners, vendors, clients, and others who occasionally need to enter the building. Does that reality mean that employees need to schlep to the office if they can't work from home?

No.

Coworking Spaces

WeWork may have popularized coworking spaces, but the concept dates back more than thirty years. British entrepreneur Mark Dixon founded Regus in Brussels in 1989.[27] His goal wasn't terribly different from that of disgraced WeWork founder Adam Neumann: to provide flexible office space to other businesses. That's it. Regus is still around today, but it sits under the umbrella of International Workplace Group (IWG plc).

Teams looking for proper work or meeting spaces can book only the hours, days, weeks, months, or years they need. And let's not minimize the Airbnb effect. CitizenM, Mandarin Oriental, and other hospitality brands have converted local coffee shops and hotel floors into workspaces that allow teams and individuals to book space easily.[28] In August 2020, Starbucks began testing a coworking space in Tokyo.[29]

Satellite Offices

Organizations looking for something more permanent than a monthly coworking lease often opt for satellite offices. Once again, this concept dates back decades.

It's time to meet Jack Nilles, the father of telecommuting. In the late '50s and '60s, he was devising reconnaissance satellites in his job as a rocket scientist. Here's the genesis of his big idea:

> Then came a career switch in the early 1970s, when Nilles shifted from rocket scientist to the director of interdisciplinary research at the University of Southern California, a position created for him so he could follow his theory that remote working, then unheard of, would be good for business and even better for the environment.
>
> Living amidst Los Angeles' notorious traffic congestion and seeing the increasing volatility around air pollution and other emerging oil and gas issues, Nilles floated the idea that office workers need not go into the company's corporate offices to be effective. He envisioned satellite offices located closer to where employees lived, the payoff being employees who are less stressed and more productive, employers saving money by forgoing expensive downtown real estate, and an ecosystem that would benefit from a reduction in commuter traffic.[30]

In 1976, Nilles penned a book: *The Telecommunications-Transportation Tradeoff: Options for Tomorrow.* Its concepts are just as relevant today as they were then, if not more so given climate change and rising gas prices.

For their part, industrial designers are licking their lips at the options that satellite offices afford.[31]

You don't have to be an astronomer to know that satellites collect information by orbiting planets and moons. (*Project Management in the Hybrid Workplace* provides much more detail about why remote and hybrid work will stick.)

Putting It All Together: Hubs and Spokes

With so many people routinely working in different places, creating coherent experiences for employees can be challenging. To be fair, a dispersed workforce poses employee and managerial obstacles absent from their traditional, synchronous cohorts.

Multiple locations and decentralized work, however, need not result in disorganization, a drop in productivity, and inefficiency. It's time to welcome a different, tech-based, and employee-friendly model of work—one predicated on hubs and spokes.* (Chapter 7 details the immersive technologies that are making virtual and dispersed work smoother.)

Adam Segal is the CEO of the real estate tech company cove. Speaking to Forbes in 2021, he describes a "centralized hub for people to come together, while also providing the choice to work from spokes."[32] Figure 2.7 visualizes this model.

Segal isn't the first to espouse this idea. Based on the workplace changes that have occurred over the past three years, adopting the Hub-Spoke Model—or at least some form of it—is essential.

---

* Despite the shared nomenclature, this concept differs from the Hub-Spoke Model of Collaboration detailed in my book *Reimagining Collaboration.*

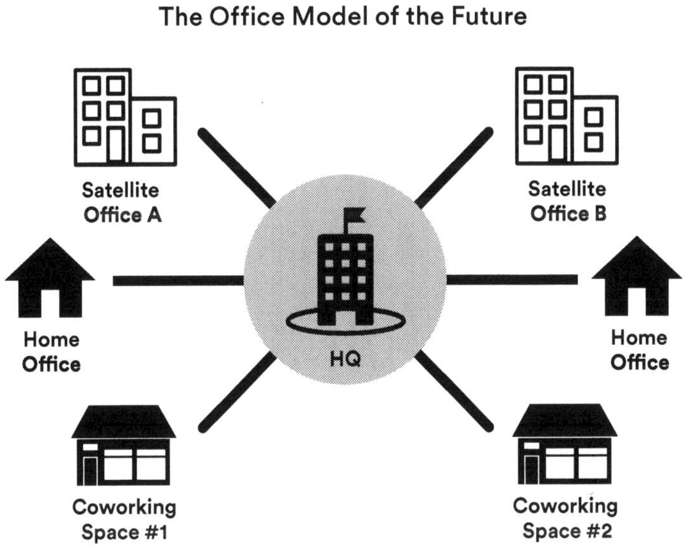

The Office Model of the Future

Figure 2.7: The Office Model of the Future

Predictions

Companies that adopt strict return-to-work policies will start hemorrhaging talent. Many will eventually reverse course after high performers begin leaving en masse.

Small business owners and execs will increasingly realize the following: just because people *can* work from home if given the choice doesn't mean they always *will*. Reasons abound. For one, not all homes provide the physical space to perform dedicated, long-term work. In mid-2020, demand for prefab backyard offices and tiny homes spiked. Lacking proper places to concentrate, homeowners began plunking down $30,000 or more to Kanga Room Systems, Plus Hus, LIV Pods, and others. Expect the use of satellite offices and coworking spaces to continue rising.

Employees generally will, within reason, accept slightly lower pay to retain their remote or hybrid status. In effect, they're buying flexibility and less commute time.

The next employee-management battle will involve *when* work occurs. It's a natural extension of being able to work hundreds or even thousands of miles away from a central office.

Expect most organizations to require employees to work from the office two or three days per week. Some workers will refuse to *ever* meet with their colleagues in person or step foot on company property. Generally speaking, managers will gladly let them walk.

Within a year of this book's publication, a Fortune 1000 company will reverse its WFH policy. At least 15 percent of its workforce will leave within one month. Firms will continue to reverse their policy changes.

In the short term, managers resistant to worker empowerment and dispersion will have to continue biting the bullet. Along with the rising wages (discussed in the next chapter), this resentment will cause organizations to accelerate the adoption of emerging technologies. (Chapters 4 through 7, inclusive, delve into which ones.)

Key Points

- Employees no longer view remote/hybrid work as a perk. During the pandemic, it morphed into a requirement.
- Much—if not most—work can take place outside of traditional offices. LinkedIn, Cisco, and Dropbox are examples of companies that revamped their offices to accommodate remote and hybrid work.
- Satellite offices and coworking spaces are affordable and flexible alternatives to expensive office renovations.

CHAPTER 3
Systemic Inflation

Seven percent won't persist, but we're unlikely to revert to two percent anytime soon.

"Sooner or later, everyone sits down to a banquet of consequences."

—ROBERT LOUIS STEVENSON

Even if you've been living under a rock or off the grid for the past two years, you've seen prices increase. The cost of everything seems to be rising these days, but some business leaders don't appear to be worried about its long-term impact.

Bahram Akradi is the founder, chairman, and CEO of Life Time, a chain of 156 upscale athletic clubs. As he told the *Wall Street Journal* in December 2022:

> If everything costs 30 percent more, then we charge 30 percent more. Our customer is someone who wants the best experience and will find a way to pay for it.[1]

Akradi isn't necessarily being arrogant. He's betting on what economists call *inelastic demand* for his company's services. That is, price increases won't cause his customers to seek alternative services. If that sounds a smidge heady or abstract, just think about gas prices. When they spiked in mid-2022, did you fill up your car only halfway at the pump?

Contrast inelastic demand with its elastic counterpart. Let's say that the cost of a monthly Netflix subscription increases while Hulu's fee remains constant. All else being equal (admittedly, a big disclaimer), consumers are more likely to cancel the former and subscribe to the latter. Figure 3.1 distinguishes between these two types of demand.

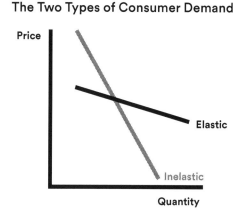

Figure 3.1: The Two Types of Consumer Demand

We've landed on the idea of a substitute good: when consumers buy more of Product X, they purchase less of Product Y. In Akradi's case, Life Time members—and I'm one of them—will grin and bear the annual increases to their already-pricey memberships. (Its Manhattan clubs charge $259 per month.)

Akradi may be right: his customers won't flock to Equinox, Planet Fitness, Orangetheory, or another health club over a 5 percent bump in monthly fees. Nor will they hire personal trainers or buy a lululemon Studio Mirror, Peloton, Tonal, or other home exercise equipment.

Customers paying for the product or services represents just one side of the inflation coin, though.

The Flip Side of Inflation

In mid-2013, Lydia Griffin—a pseudonym—accepted a position at a large public university in the midwestern US. (We'll call it LMU here.) As a front office manager, the high school graduate earned $35,000 per year. The money wasn't great for someone in her early thirties, but Griffin took the job for other reasons. She was keen on getting her bachelor's degree. LMU offered its full-time staff significantly reduced tuition.

Griffin soon began taking classes. In 2017, she graduated with a BS in life sciences. During that time, she also received a promotion and a few modest salary increases.

Historically, LMU relied on reduced tuition and other non-monetary benefits to attract and retain its employees. For the past fifteen years, the university rarely doled out cost-of-living adjustments. Merit increases at performance review time were typically meager, even for faculty members who received promotions.

Despite paying submarket wages, employee turnover was relatively minimal. Few people were making bank but, with inflation practically nonexistent, at least LMU employees' purchasing power didn't erode.

All that started changing in the spring of 2021. As Figure 3.2 displays, inflation began to spike.

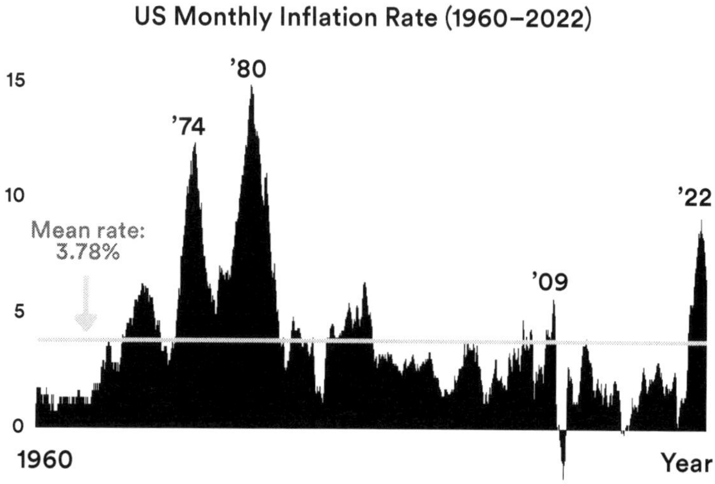

US Monthly Inflation Rate (1960–2022)

Figure 3.2: US Monthly Inflation Rate (1960–2022), Source: US Bureau of Labor Statistics, https://tinyurl.com/bls-ps2

Everything suddenly seemed to cost more: groceries, airline tickets, rent, and even Netflix subscriptions. Like most organizations, LMU started experiencing second-order effects—particularly a noticeable uptick in voluntary employee attrition.

LMU's board of regents needed to staunch the bleeding. In June 2021, it approved a 3.5 percent increase in employee salaries. The board was unaccustomed to allocating so much of the school's budget to compensation. It felt that its move sufficiently addressed the rising cost of goods and services.

It didn't.

That month, annualized US inflation clocked in at 7 percent—twice the rate of LMU's forthcoming employee salary adjustment.[2] Workers who remained at the school would be taking *de facto* pay cuts. Well-remunerated administrators, tenured professors, and football coaches would be fine, but rank-and-file employees like Griffin didn't fall into that group.

Griffin had been content at LMU but was entering a different point in her life. Since joining LMU, she'd shared an apartment with two roommates. As she approached her fortieth birthday, she wanted to get her own place. Her paycheck wasn't getting her as far as it did two years ago, and her current salary didn't allow her to spend even more on rent. Something had to give.

Griffin began poking around on job boards and interviewing for new positions. Why wait until an economic downturn to try and switch jobs? Because of the tight labor market, she didn't have to look long. She ultimately accepted a position at a local healthcare company with a salary 15 percent higher than what she'd been earning. The increase allowed her to finally rent a studio apartment.

LMU's board hopes that inflation reverts to its prepandemic level. Just about every banker, sane politician, business owner, and employee understandably does.

Lamentably, it won't—at least not anytime soon.

Why High(er) Inflation Is Here to Stay

Since 1960, the mean end-of-year inflation rate in the US has been 3.78 percent. Only once during the past decade did that number top 3 percent. (See Figure 3.2.) In other words, we've lived through an extended era of cheap money that has come to an end.

The idea that we can *permanently* solve or extinguish inflation is absurd—and only a fool would argue otherwise. That grim reality doesn't mean that central banks can't try to tame it. They can, and they are. The Federal Reserve and its chair, Jerome Powell, have moved aggressively to contain it in the US. As of this writing, it appears to be working. We're still experiencing inflation, but it's finally beginning to taper off.

Still, there's a limit. We should see inflation drop from its current, annualized level of 6.5 percent for the twelve months ending in December 2022. We're unlikely to return to the minuscule rates of the past twenty years (read: 2 percent) anytime soon. As *The Economist* put it in July 2022, "inflation looks likely to stay above the pre-pandemic norm."[3]

Here's a short, simplified explanation of why.

The Massive Increase in the Money Supply

A capitalist economy can be managed two ways. I'll focus on democracies here and the US specifically—at least under normal circumstances.[*]

Politicians rely on fiscal policy. They set tax rates that determine how much income corporations and individuals can keep, what they can deduct, and the like. For their part, central banks want to maintain stable prices, curb inflation, and keep people employed. To achieve these admirable goals, they tinker with interest rates and manipulate the money supply. The latter represents the volume of currency that the public holds.

---

[*] I'm leaving aside emergency programs, such as the Troubled Asset Relief Program (TARP) to save the economy during the subprime crisis in October 2008.

COVID-19 cast a pall over the economy. In April 2020, more than 23 million people found themselves out of work, up threefold from 7.8 million the previous month.[4] Businesses across the country closed, unemployment claims exploded, and people were justifiably panicking.

What to do? How could governments avert a full-blown crisis?

Changes to corporate and individual tax rates would have failed to yield immediate relief. Issuing trillions of dollars in stimulus checks to business owners and individuals would be effective—and that's precisely what the government did. With respect to the latter, the Internal Revenue Service issued three Economic Impact Payments during the coronavirus pandemic to eligible individuals as follows:

- $1,200 in April 2020
- $600 in December 2020/January 2021
- $1,400 in March 2021[5]

I want to focus on the end result of all this financial maneuvering, so I'll skip over the mechanics and logistics of stimulus checks. (At a high level, they involve the US Treasury Department, bonds, and the Fed.*)

Mohamed El-Erian is a world-renowned economist who has forgotten ten times more about US monetary policy than I'll ever know. In December 2022, he appeared on Ezra Klein's eponymous podcast and dropped the following nugget:

> The Fed's broadest measure of the money supply, called M2, is more than $21.6 trillion today, up from $15.5 trillion in February 2020.[6]

---

* Visit https://tinyurl.com/stim-explanation if you want to know more.

Think about that for a moment. The number of dollars in circulation has grown nearly 40 percent within the past two years. And what do Americans tend to do with their money?

Lots of things, but "put it in the bank" or "save it for a rainy day" don't rate high on the list. Again, don't believe me.

As of June 2021, the US ranked fifteenth out of thirty-four OECD countries for the percentage of disposable income saved.[7]

We Americans spend our money, damn it. Great, but opening up our wallets generally drives prices up when supply remains constant. Now let me add a few wrinkles. What if demand for goods outpaces their availability? And what if supply doesn't stay constant but *declines*?

The correct answer here is *Yikes*.

Supply Chain Issues

Amazon may have perfected next-day shipping and made it *seem* simple. Just hit the Buy Now with 1 Click button and wait for your item to arrive. Easy peasy, right?

Nothing could be further from the truth.

It's difficult to appreciate the mind-numbing complexity of our modern, global supply chain. For my money, the best book on the subject is Christopher Mims's *Arriving Today: From Factory to Front Door—Why Everything Has Changed about How and What We Buy*.

For years, the global supply chain ran like clockwork—until it didn't. In no particular order, we endured a perfect storm of:

- COVID-19.
- A tariff-happy US president.
- Bottlenecks at West Coast docks.
- Increased US-China geopolitical tensions.

- The Ever Given megaship jamming the Suez Canal for six excruciating days.[8]

Oh, and shipping costs rapidly escalated. Statista reported in March 2022 that "based on aggregated data for all trade lanes, shipping a forty-foot container cost around $8,200, up more than 600 percent compared to two years before."[9] To be fair, container freight prices have receded considerably since then. The key lesson: just because transportation costs are low now doesn't mean they have to remain that way.

Add it all up, and is it any wonder that we started running out of baby food, toilet paper, and other essentials? When essentials did arrive on shelves, they didn't last long and frequently cost more—in some cases, much more.

Just a temporary blip, right?

Probably not. Consider the elephant in the room: what if US-China relations break bad or China invades Taiwan? The consequences would be dire—and instantaneous. As but one example, we could face a shortage of chips that power our appliances, smartphones, computers, kids' gaming consoles, and just about every piece of electronics we own. The subtitle of Chris Miller's bestselling 2022 book *Chip War* perfectly sums up the issue: *The Fight for the World's Most Critical Technology.*

To their credit, government officials and chipmakers' CXOs recognize the risk. They've been working to minimize US dependence on Chinese semiconductor manufacturing, as the following examples illustrate:

- In May 2020, Taiwan Semiconductor, the world's most valuable semiconductor company, agreed to build a $12 billion factory in Arizona.[10]

- Samsung announced plans to build a $17 billion chip plant in Texas. [11]
- After playing footsie with Texas, Intel decided to build a $20 billion chip factory in Ohio. [12]
- Apple has begun making the iPhone 14 in India, marking a big shift in its China-centric manufacturing strategy. [13] It has also increasingly brought chip design in-house over the past decade.

CEOs looking to reshore their operations today will find no shortage of governors willing to lavish generous tax breaks on their companies if they opt to bring jobs to their states. Still, one doesn't transform a sophisticated, global supply chain in a month or a year. The idea that the US will soon be chip-independent isn't sanguine; it's risible.

Yes, manufacturing in America translates into lower shipping costs, but so what? American workers earn far more than their Chinese counterparts. It's hard to imagine a future in which most consumer items cost less than they do now. This means two things. First, inflation. Second, returning to the subject of Chapter 1, if you think that reshoring increases the power of American employees and unions, trust your instincts.

And that's not all. The recent supply chain shocks are driving up prices in another way.

The Great Inventory Trade-Off

For generations, citizens in industrialized societies have taken convenience, safety, and public health for granted. Historically speaking, not *that* long ago, the very act of drinking water could result in death.

In London, between 1848 and 1854, cholera killed 25,000 people because people dumped raw sewage into the River Thames. Although people used the very same river for drinking water, they didn't know any better.[14]

In his 2017 book *Progress: Ten Reasons to Look Forward to the Future*, Johan Norberg reveals this bizarre tidbit:

> In 1900, horses supposedly fouled New York City streets with more than 2.5 million pounds of manure and 60,000 gallons of urine daily. The streets were carpeted with the stuff.

Norberg is spot-on, writing later in the book, "The truth is that, if we care to turn the clock back, the good old days were awful."

We're not used to visiting supermarkets and big-box retailers only to find empty shelves. We want what we want, and we want it *now*. Comedian Ronny Chieng hysterically and perfectly captures this sentiment in his Netflix special *Asian Comedian Destroys America!* in a bit about Amazon Prime.* Let's just say that we're not very patient.

As consumers faced unprecedented shortages of essentials, many predictably took to social media to post photos of empty shelves. (Yes, you can search for #emptyshelves on Twitter.) Some politically charged memes went viral, with hashtags excoriating the president ostensibly responsible for the problem.

Although the target of their venom was often misplaced, consumers' frustration is understandable. "I *love* driving all the way to Target or Walmart only to discover that I can't find what I need," said no one ever.

---

* Watch it yourself at https://tinyurl.com/ps-Chieng.

Some grocery and drug stores hung tarps over these eyesores as a temporary remedy. (Subtle it was not.) Twenty years ago, perhaps consumers would have bitten the bullet. Joe Sixpack would just return to Safeway to buy ketchup, toilet paper, or other out-of-stock items. In an era of smartphones and ecommerce, however, the efficacy of that stratagem is questionable at best. Disaffected customers can—and frequently do—just whip out their phones, launch the Amazon or Target app, and make the purchase right then and there. (Yeah, showrooming is a thing.)*

Compared to tarps and "Sorry, we're out" signs, keeping more inventory on hand represents a better, more sustainable solution to these thorny inventory challenges. Unfortunately, it's also a more expensive solution, and companies of all kinds will pass these storage costs on to their customers.

At first glance, Kodak and Olaplex don't appear to have much in common. The former makes "industry-leading products and services for commercial print, packaging, publishing, manufacturing, and entertainment."[15] The latter's offerings include shampoos, oils, and masks that purportedly repair and prevent hair damage. We're not talking about Lowes and The Home Depot here.

Despite serving wildly different markets, the two firms are adopting the same product strategy: hold more stuff (aka, resilience over efficiency). In May 2022, Kodak held

> around six months of inventory, compared with three months before the supply-chain challenges began, Mr.

---

* Showrooming occurs when customers at physical stores whip out their phones and compare prices with Amazon and other sites. Execs at these retail outlets hate the practice, but they're effectively incapable of preventing it.

Bullwinkle said. During the first quarter, the company re-ported $247 million in net inventory, up more than 12% from the prior-year period.[16]

More formally, the standard corporate practice involved the cost-effective "just-in-time" inventory management. In recent years, its "just-in-case" counterpart has triumphed. If that means higher storage costs, so be it. Customers will foot the bill.

Increased Employee Mobility

Inflation is a complicated beast; factors contribute to it. Count employee salaries among the usual suspects. Scenarios vary, but it can work like this:

1. Prices increase.
2. Workers ask for higher wages to restore their purchasing power.
3. To keep profits humming, companies in turn raise prices.
4. Employees again ask for pay increases.
5. The cycle continues indefinitely.

Figure 3.3 shows a visual of the self-perpetuating phenomenon that economists refer to as a *wage-price spiral.*

The Wage-Price Spiral

Figure 3.3: The Wage-Price Spiral

The term isn't new; it first appeared in print in 1937.[17] The idea that wages and prices enter an interminable, pernicious feedback loop gravely concerns the Federal Reserve in its battle to curtail inflation. As of this writing, the jury is still out on whether it's happening now. Some evidence suggests that the tight labor market may *not* be pushing prices higher.[18]

That's certainly possible, but the prevalence and acceptance of remote and hybrid work may make taming the wage-price spiral more challenging than usual.

To switch jobs in the past, workers sometimes needed to move their families, sell their homes, and find new schools for their children. In the case of white-collar workers, companies typically offered generous relocation packages, even to college graduates. (In the case of senior executives, it wasn't uncommon for one's future employer to purchase the new hire's current home as part of the deal.)

To some extent, all these factors deterred employee mobility. They added friction and prevented some folks from accepting new positions. On a personal level, one of my friends told me a few years back, "Yes, I can make 10 percent more if I move, but my spouse will kill me if I ask us to move cross-country again."

Thanks to remote and hybrid work, those impediments to employee mobility aren't as pronounced as they were in 2017. In most cases, they've vanished.

Pent-Up Consumer Demand

Thanks to lockdown, we couldn't see our friends and family. Sure, Zoom was better than nothing, but videoconferencing just wasn't the same as being in the presence of our loved ones.

Local, state, and national governments eventually lifted travel and gathering restrictions, unleashing the enormous, pent-up demand to travel. Many have publicly declared that they're "done with COVID." (It's an understandable sentiment, but COVID certainly isn't done with us.)

Think about the precipitous rise in the price of airline tickets. Writing for CNBC in May 2022, Brett Holzhauer notes that:

> In the last year, the consumer price index for airline tickets has shot up by 25 percent—the largest jump since the Federal Reserve of St. Louis began tracking the index in 1989. In April alone, airfares spiked 18.6 percent, according to the Bureau of Labor Statistics.[19]

According to established economic orthodoxy, those price increases mean that fewer people will get on planes. (See the discussion earlier in this chapter on elastic demand.)

In fact, the opposite has occurred.

The Bank of America Institute describes itself as "a think tank dedicated to uncovering insights that move business and society forward." Its May 2022 survey revealed that, despite its price hikes, consumer spending at airlines and travel agencies rose an astonishing 60 percent in the past year.[20]

Equipped with that information, what would you do if you ran Delta, JetBlue, or American Airlines? Would you offer free in-flight Wi-Fi? Would you discount fares or eliminate baggage check-in fees?

I didn't think so.

Perhaps air travel is becoming a Veblen good—a product whose demand increases as its price *increases*.*

Rents on the Rise

Americans spent a good deal of their disposable income on rent. Here are some telling stats from the 2020 US Census Bureau:

- 46 percent of renters spent 30 percent or more of their income on housing.
- 23 percent spent at least half of their income on rent.[21]

And it's not just cities, although that's where you'll find some of the most eye-popping increases. Rents are soaring pretty much everywhere in the country.[22] Myriad millennials would love to swap their monthly rent checks for mortgage payments, but they can't. Colossal levels of student debt, a white-hot housing market, and stratospheric interest rates have made homeownership virtually unattainable for millions of young Americans. Collectively, these factors explain much of why a majority of young adults in the US are living with their parents.[23]

This type of thing doesn't happen often. The last time occurred during the Great Depression.

The Rise of Salary Transparency

The American writer Stewart Brand is best known for uttering these five words: "Information wants to be free."

He wasn't talking specifically about pay ranges for different jobs. Still, Brand's well-worn aphorism applies here as well.

As of January 2023, an increasing number of state and local governments have passed laws mandating different levels of pay

---

* Named after the American economist Thorstein Veblen.

transparency.* The list includes California, Colorado, Connecticut, Maryland, Nevada, New York, Ohio, Rhode Island, and Washington. Payscale reports that roughly one-quarter of all US workers now live in a place in which employers must legally share pay ranges for different positions.[24] I suspect that that number won't decrease in the years ahead; if anything, it'll continue to rise.

The specific statutes vary. At a high level, they "require companies to be prepared to disclose salary information to job applicants."[25] Ideally, publicizing this information will reduce race and gender-based pay gaps.

Ideally, this legislation will help accomplish their worthy goals. Still, there's reason to be skeptical. As Matthew Boyle of Bloomberg astutely observes, "when it comes to measures designed to redress inequities in pay, the law of unintended consequences often comes into play."[26]

Count increased employee requests for raises among these consequences. A simple example illustrates a scenario that has played out numerous times over the past eighteen months.

By way of background, compensation and HR folks typically group employees into different *salary bands.* These categories transcend individual departments. Another alternative is the compa-ratio, "a measure that expresses current pay rates as a percentage of range midpoints."[27]

Meet Lucy. She's worked as a finance director at a small midwestern retailer for the past three years. She finds herself in the same *salary* or *pay band* as Ian, her counterpart in marketing. Ian abruptly retires. The company quickly posts the job, along with its legally required salary range of $80,000 to $120,000.

---

* To see the updated list, go to https://tinyurl.com/sal-ps-payscale.

Lucy determines the range's midpoint, divides her salary by it, and sees that it's less than one. Figure 3.4 shows this basic algebra.

Simple Compa-Ratio Example

Salary Band	Minimum	Midpoint	Maximum
D	$80,000	$100,000	$120,000

Lucy's Compa-Ratio: $90,000/$100,000 = 0.9

Figure 3.4: Simple Compa-Ratio Example

She realizes that she makes less than the band's midpoint.* She's always suspected that she earned less than her peers. Equipped with this information, she talks to her manager, Pete, about her compensation. After some back-and-forth, Pete reluctantly raises her salary to $100,000. He doesn't want Lucy to quit.

The moral of the story: oodles of already empowered employees in a tight labor market will soon realize how much they're making compared to what they *could* be earning.

Here's the headline: pay transparency laws attempt to advance admirable goals, and I support them. Still, they may inadvertently intensify inflation.

So What?

For all the reasons described in this chapter, expecting the quick return of near-zero inflation anytime soon is a fool's errand. Some level is here to stay for the foreseeable future, at least to a far greater extent than we've recently seen.

---

* Note that the midpoint need not be the mean, never mind the median or the mode. Also, to be fair, many HR departments willingly share salary band and compensation information with their employees.

What's the big whoop?

Don't naysay this increase and assume that your organization or industry can indefinitely pass these costs to consumers through higher prices. Rare is the product or service that benefits from inelastic demand. Moreover, this notion isn't a binary; price elasticity has degrees. At some point, the majority of us start looking at substitutes. George may prefer to buy salmon, but he can only afford tuna.

Declining sales at some point typically yield lower profits, layoffs, and other cutbacks. Increased inflation also ultimately results in higher interest rates. When the cost of borrowing money increases, senior executives need to be more discerning with the projects they authorize. Typically, only those with higher expected rates of return make the cut.

Finally, let's say that by some miracle inflation returns in 2023 to its microscopic levels from the Great Recession to mid-2021. The past eighteen months have reminded us of its power. It's absurd to think that any country, politician, or central bank can permanently "solve" inflation, at least without dire consequences.

So, yes, it matters.

𝍩 𝍪

Faced with empowered employees, sky-high attrition, and elevated labor costs, employers aren't standing still. As we'll see in the next two chapters, they're taking steps that will, down the road, let them rein in costs and reduce their dependency on fickle workers.

Key Points

- For a variety of reasons over the past dozen years, we've benefited from near-zero inflation. That era is over.
- Some corporations in pivotal industries are reshoring to alleviate inventory issues and geopolitical risks. Although understandable and arguably beneficial in the long term, the move will likely increase short- and medium-term inflationary pressures.
- Increased employee mobility, remote work, and dispersed workplaces mean that employees can chase higher wages, frequently without uprooting their families in the process.

CHAPTER 4

Automation

More dominoes are starting to fall.

"Automation is driving the decline of banal and repetitive tasks."
—AMBER RUDD

In late December 2022, residents in Fort Worth, Texas, walked into a local McDonald's. Most of them expected the normal drill, but they soon discovered something strange.

No one seemed to be minding the restaurant.

The night manager at this Golden Arches didn't forget to lock up the night before. Employees weren't picketing.

Patrons could still order, pay for, and receive their Big Macs. There was a catch: neither activity required any human interaction. A combination of sophisticated software and machines received customer orders, prepared the food, and served the meals via a conveyor belt. Fans of the cartoon *The Jetsons* saw the modern-day equivalent of its Foodarackacycle food-serving machine. Foodiemunster's TikTok video, "New Robot McDonald's Is Freaking People Out," went viral.*

The Fort Worth franchise was the first to test this high-tech concept. In the words of its owner, Keith Vanecek,

> The technology in this restaurant not only allows us to serve our customers in new, innovative ways, it gives our restaurant team the ability to concentrate more on order speed and accuracy, which makes the experience more enjoyable for everyone.[1]

Vanecek may be right. Full disclosure: I haven't visited his specific Mickey D's. Still, he omits a few of the benefits that he expects to realize from his decked-out, worker-free fast-food joint. Machines aren't about to form labor unions or strike for higher wages. Robots won't become sentient and go all *Westworld* on us—at least, we hope not.

Although plenty of people expressed their outrage, others simply dismissed the story. After all, how hard is it to flip burgers? Answer: not very. I did it after school in the seventh grade for six months.

Automation may *eventually* affect your industry or employer, but there's no way that robots or software can do *your* job, right?

Maybe, but probably not. Whether we like it or not, some level of automation is coming to every workplace—even yours. What's more, the force is approaching with greater speed and intensity these days.

---

* Watch a YouTube video of it at https://tinyurl.com/the-9-mcds.

Automation in the Workplace

Companies replacing humans with machines is nothing new. Let's turn back the clock a century:

> From AT&T's founding in the mid–1870s to the late 1910s, telephone calls were manually connected by operators working the switchboards at telephone exchanges around the country.*
>
> But between 1920 and 1940, telephone exchanges serving more than half the US telephone network were mechanized, replacing most functions of local operators.[2]

Despite the history of workplace automation, there seemed to be an especially icky aspect to the Fort Worth McDonald's. Articles and videos about it immediately elicited strong reactions online. (What doesn't these days?) As for why, here's one theory: the story tapped into our growing fears that machines are gunning for our jobs.

In December 2018, Pew Research Center conducted an extensive survey on Americans' views on automation.[3] Most relevant here is the question, What do they expect to happen by 2050? The results are fascinating:

- 82 percent say that robots and computers "will definitely or probably" perform much of the work that people currently do.
- 76 percent believe that automation will exacerbate the gap between the rich and the poor.
- Nearly half say that tech-based workplace automation has mostly hurt US workers.

---

* Go nuts at https://tinyurl.com/9-switchboards.

Most Americans fear the effects of automation and artificial intelligence (discussed in the next chapter). Okay, but should they?

Klaus Schwab surely thinks so. As the German economist and chairman of the World Economic Forum wrote in his 2016 book *The Fourth Industrial Revolution*:

> Many different categories of work, particularly those that involve mechanically repetitive and precise manual labor, have already been automated. Many others will follow, as computing power continues to grow exponentially.
>
> Sooner than most anticipate, the work of professions as different as lawyers, financial analysts, doctors, journalists, accountants, insurance underwriters or librarians may be partly or completely automated.

One oft-cited 2013 study estimates that 47 percent of total US employment is at risk of "computerization."[4] Interestingly, the probability of mechanization correlates negatively with education and income. There are no guarantees, but jobs that pay big bucks and require university degrees are more immune to advances in technology, AI, software, and robotics, at least for now.

And the data indicates that automation is indeed gaining steam. For instance, in August 2020, McKinsey released the latest findings of its Global Survey on Automation. Two-thirds of organizations reported at least beginning to automate one or more business functions or units. The number in 2018 was 57 percent.[5] Figure 4.1 shows a more detailed breakdown.

Figure 4.1: Organizations Are Increasingly Automating Business Functions
Data from McKinsey. Figure from the author.

Figure 4.1 focuses on business functions, underscoring the reality that *automation* is a broad category. Let's break it down a bit.

A Deliberately Simple Model of Automation

The International Organization for Standardization develops and maintains standards for myriad categories, including medical devices, automobiles, and shoe sizes.[6] Search for a universally accepted definition of *automation,* however, and you'll go wanting. Google "types of automation," and you'll quickly find yourself going down a rabbit hole.

For our purposes, it's best to think of work-related automation in terms of outcomes. In other words, *what* exactly are we automating? Let's ponder the following five general categories:

1. **Task:** Movie theaters no longer need to employ people to sell popcorn.[7] Not to be outdone, robots can also now make pizzas.*

---

* Yes, you can do that. See https://tinyurl.com/9-ps-pizza.

2. **Process:** Some organizations have employed AP automation technology to minimize the number of people needed to pay their vendors.
3. **Entire job:** The days of truck drivers might be numbered.[8]
4. **Department or function:** Can we use AI to automate content moderation? Elon Musk seems to think so at Twitter.[9] Meta and YouTube execs have felt the same way for varying degrees over the years.
5. **Industry:** Will translators exist in twenty years? Not if companies like Otter.ai have anything to do with it.

All else being equal, as we move down the list from *task* to *industry*, the difficulty of fully automating the category increases. Figure 4.2 displays this intentionally simplistic model.

An Overly Simplistic Model of Automation

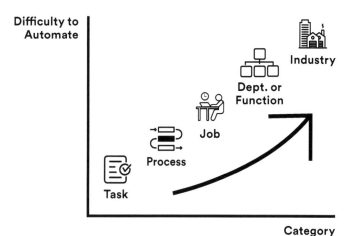

Figure 4.2: An Overly Simplistic Model of Automation

This construct is admittedly imperfect. For example, it may be harder to automate a unique and complex task than a straightforward, routine process.

Generally speaking, though, Figure 4.2 is a useful model. Processes consist of a bunch of tasks. The VP who has automated all her department's manual activities has probably streamlined its operations as much as possible. Automate enough processes in someone's job, and the need for that headcount goes *poof.* You get my drift.

The disparate examples cited earlier and described in Figure 4.2 are instructive. Still, what about a typical, more cohesive example? Table 4.1 provides a holistic look at this work hierarchy in the context of running payroll.

Item	Examples
Tasks	Collecting, reviewing, and approving employee hours and time records. Resolving errors with employees and managers.
Processes	Calculating employee overtime and taxes. Printing checks and remitting direct deposits to employee banks. Closing payroll and writing entries to the general ledger.
Jobs	Payroll manager, supervisor, or clerks.
Responsible department	Payroll, of course. Note that, in some firms, the Payroll Department falls under Accounting.
Industries	ADP, Paychex, and Gusto are just some of the companies that provide this service for companies that outsource their payroll. Some have expanded their offerings and rebranded as professional employer organizations.

Table 4.1: Payroll Work Hierarchy

To state the obvious, payroll tasks, processes, and jobs have morphed over time. In the 1970s and 1980s, employees filled out detailed paper timesheets. New technologies mean that only the most hidebound organizations continue to rely on paper and calculators. Employees have swiped badges for years. High-tech timeclocks precisely capture this data, sometimes tens of thousands of times per day.

Put differently, we've been automating tasks and processes for decades. Unlike blockchain (discussed in Chapter 6), automation is *already* commonplace. It will intensify, in some part, because few people doubt its benefits.

Making Automation Happen

The English sci-fi writer Arthur C. Clarke once astutely observed, "Any sufficiently advanced technology is indistinguishable from magic."

Automation technologies have qualified as *sufficiently advanced* for a while now. At the same time, though, automation is anything but monolithic. Different tools serve different purposes and audiences; one size certainly doesn't fit all. Let's explore some of the most popular buckets of contemporary automation tools.

Macros

It's natural to think of automation as the sole purview of proper techies. Nothing could be further from the truth. Power users and other nondevelopers have long been able to automate the hell out of manual tasks—at least ones in the Microsoft universe.

Microsoft launched its Macro Assembler for Excel way back in 1992. Visual Basic for Applications allowed Windows users[*] to effectively create bespoke mini-programs. Recording macros allowed users to automate repetitive activities in Excel and, later, Access, Word, and PowerPoint.

Robotic Process Automation

Ask forgiveness, not permission.

---

[*] With respect to macros, Mac users were second-class citizens for a very long time.

Those four words accurately sum up Uber's chaotic early days. The startup aggressively set up shop in new countries and cities around the world. Mike Isaac's 2019 book *Super Pumped* is my favorite on the company.

In 2017, Uber's board finally shitcanned its volatile CEO, Travis Kalanick. It was high time for mature leadership. Enter Dara Khosrowshahi. The former head honcho at Expedia knew he had his work cut out for him. His new employer had lost a cool $4.46 billion in 2017.[10] *Billion.* After getting a lay of the land, Khosrowshahi started identifying ways for Uber to finally, you know, turn a profit without resulting to accounting chicanery.

How about automation?

Khosrowshahi had assumed control well after Uber expanded its coverage far beyond San Francisco in its quest for world domination. The logistics of rapidly launching in so many countries posed plenty of logistical challenges that ambitious disruptors like Uber minimize or ignore altogether. (Move fast and break things, as they say in Silicon Valley.)

For example, like all companies, Uber needed to pay its vendors. Procedures that worked in the US, however, wouldn't fly in the UK or China. Basic questions included:

- How could the company ensure, to the extent possible, that it had synchronized its geographic operations?
- How could senior managers rapidly view an accurate snapshot of accounts payable?
- How could the company reduce the hours required to run its global AP department?
- How could it reduce errors and ensure a greater level of accuracy?

At a high level, through automation. But how exactly?

Uber's business was—and is—nothing if not complex. As a result, it needed the equivalent of sophisticated software robots to automate the manual, rule-based, and repetitive activities that spanned its internal systems. In other words, it needed a technology called *robotic process automation*. (HFS Research founder Phil Fersht originally coined the term in 2012, but RPA implementations have only recently started to gain steam.)

Some experts view RPA as the next iteration of macros or, if you like, macros on steroids. For Uber, the choice was a no-brainer. Foolish is the soul who tries to run a company then valued at $69 billion on Microsoft Access and Excel.[11]

Table 4.2 compares traditional macros with RPA.

Attribute	Traditional Macro	RPA
Birth year	1992	2012
Application or system scope	Limited to a single application or, at best, across different applications within a suite. For example, people can automatically distribute Microsoft Excel workbooks as Outlook attachments via Access.	Not limited to individual websites, enterprise systems, and applications.
Ability to mimic human interactions	Somewhat limited.	Far more robust.
Technical resources required	Minimal.	More extensive.
Time and cost to deploy	Short and cheap.	Can be extensive and expensive.
Primary orientation	Task.	Process.

Attribute	Traditional Macro	RPA
Ability for the technology to independently learn	None.	When coupled with AI and, specifically, machine learning, RPA tools can learn how to improve existing business processes.
Level of automation	Limited to individual users or, at best, small teams.	Effectively unlimited. Individuals, groups, and departments in large enterprises can reap significant benefits from modern RPA tools.

Table 4.2: Overview of Traditional Macros vs. RPA

Note the limited scope of Table 4.2. I'm not implying that it accurately summarizes two decades of workplace or enterprise automation. I'm merely comparing different facets of two popular automation technologies.

Let's get back to Uber's use of RPA. The company worked with Accenture and the software vendor UIPath to modernize its AP department. Here are some of the deets:

Like most companies starting their RPA journey, Uber started automating financial processes. In fact, the Accenture team still reports to the CFO. After three years, Uber has more than 100 automations in production, which saves Uber an estimated $10 million per year.

"We've been able to automate invoicing for over 80 customers across seven main portals that we use daily, which raises customer satisfaction as well as decreas[es] errors," said Kasumi Billington, Finance Operations for Uber Freight. "We began managing less than 20% of our invoices through automation two years ago, and now we're able to issue over 70% of our portal invoices monthly. With a reduced number of errors, thanks to automation, team members can now focus on problem-solving rather than just transactional tasks."[12]

Martin Cavas is an RPA engineer based out of the Netherlands. I spoke to him over Zoom while researching this book. A few years back, he worked at a financial services firm. The company relied extensively on data entry, increasing labor costs while decreasing data quality. Its manual processes meant that customer requests and support tickets took far too long to resolve. Even worse, the repetitive and frustrating administrative tasks frustrated employees.

It was a hot mess.

The firm's management tasked a small group to begin a multiyear RPA initiative. The team started automating manual processes and work. Fast-forward six years. The new technology and redesigned business processes have saved the company more than four million person-hours and tens of millions of dollars.

Along with UIPath, Automation Anywhere is one of the most prominent RPA vendors. Here are just a few examples of its clients' impressive results:

- Bancolombia reduced provisioning costs by $19 million.[13]
- KeyBank automatically processed 40,000 documents.[14]
- The UK's National Health Service decreased the time employees spent on manual data entry by 95 percent.[15]

As is usually the case with new tech, the successes of early RPA adopters are starting to embolden more conservative organizations.

Early skepticism and ignorance around RPA are starting to erode because its benefits have become less abstract. RPA is squarely on the radar of many organizations today. Exhibit A: Gartner predicts that worldwide spending on RPA will top $3 billion in 2023.[16] Figure 4.3 shows its steady increase.

Worldwide RPA End-User Spending Forecast (Billions of US Dollars)

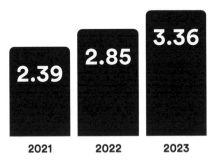

Figure 4.3: Worldwide RPA End-User Spending Forecast (Billions of US Dollars) Source: Gartner

Forrester Research is even more bullish on the RPA market. The firm predicts that it will reach $22 billion by 2025.[17]

Regression Testing

Modern coders may not recognize his name, but they owe a great deal of gratitude to David L. Parnas. In the late 1970s, the Canadian computer scientist, software engineer, and fellow Carnegie Mellon alum started thinking about ways to "avoid costly and time-consuming debugging sessions."[18] Parnas soon invented regression testing. Think of it as a way of determining whether new code breaks old code.

While undoubtedly beneficial, early methods of regression testing were manual and cumbersome. Even back then, programmers despised those two words. What comes next won't surprise anyone who has spent more than an hour with a proper techie: automation.

In the early 1980s, the use of *automated* regression testing tools started becoming more prevalent. Automation allowed developers to reduce the time required to test their changes and new code by orders of magnitude.

By the end of the twentieth century, regression testing had graduated from *optional* to *essential.* The following sidebar explains why.

Factorials and the Need for Automated Testing

Say that you work as a software developer at a midsized retail company. Customers have been clamoring to pay for items online via Stripe. Your manager has asked you to build that feature into the company's website and mobile app.

A month later, you've completed the work—or at least, you think so. Ready to launch, right?

Hardly. If you're worth your salt as a programmer, you don't just assume that your code will seamlessly work everywhere. It's time to test it. You want to ensure not only that the new functionality works but that your additions and changes didn't muck up features that previously worked. How much time will testing take?

Before addressing that question, imagine a much simpler world with only two different smartphones: an iPhone and a Samsung Galaxy. Each phone can run two different operating systems and two different browsers. In total, there are eight possible combinations. ($2^3 = 8$.)

In this simplified scenario, performing manual tests would be laborious but feasible. Say that you tested each combination for an hour. It would make for a full—if bland—day.

Now let's return to reality. Think about all the different types of computers, operating systems, and browsers. Now add all smartphones and tablets and their OSs, browsers, and apps. You're talking about hundreds of thousands or even millions of combinations. Dizzy yet? (Factorials are powerful things.)

Today, sophisticated automated testing frameworks can perform hundreds of tests per second. Tools such as Selenium efficiently pinpoint bugs and inefficient blocks of code. Even better, programmers can typically run both serial and parallel tests on apps and websites.

For this reason, developers automate as much of their regression testing as possible. Mainstream development frameworks either ship with native regression testing capability or allow developers to easily integrate third-party tools. Both statements are often true.

For example, consider Ruby. Released nearly three decades ago, it remains a popular general-purpose programming language.[19] Ruby on Rails, initially released in 2004, serves as its related full-stack web application framework. In effect, Rails provides the essential plumbing to build contemporary apps in Ruby: databases, web services, and web pages. Rails developers typically use Minitest or RSpec for regression testing. Some use both.

A few notes about automated testing frameworks (ATFs) are in order. First, just like RPA software, automation doesn't just magically happen out of the box. Setting up ATFs for a specific website or application can take a significant amount of time. Also, experienced coders know that even the most robust ATFs don't obviate occasional one-off or manual tests.

It's no overstatement to claim that the relatively obscure practice of automated regression testing has changed everything. Without it, I can safely say three things. First, software would be much, much buggier. Second, companies wouldn't release nearly as much of it. Third, new features and applications would arrive much slower than they do now.

As we'll see in the next chapter, tools like GitHub Copilot let software engineers churn out code and find bugs even more quickly.

Other Custom Solutions and APIs

Software developers don't just use automation to conduct more efficient and reliable regression tests; they embed it into their creations to save users valuable time. (Imagine having to maintain separate usernames and passwords for Gmail, YouTube, and Google Workspace. Ditto for iCloud, Apple Music, and AppleTV+.)

Powerful application programming interfaces allow developers to build apps quickly. API calls underpin a good chunk of our favorite apps, but they often facilitate automation too.

I'm no developer, but a few times over my career, I've used an API call to save myself a few hours of grueling manual work. The following sidebar explains one of those instances.

Saving Time With Python

During my years as a college professor, I forced the students to use Slack for sharing content, asking me questions, and much more.[20] I created fresh workspaces for each of my four sections. Unfortunately, Slack didn't natively integrate with Canvas, our learning management system.

As a result, for group projects, I had to manually create both the student groups in Canvas and the corresponding channels in Slack. By hand, I then had to add all students to each of them and ensure they were in sync.

Yawn.

I found and tweaked a simple Python script that magically took that data from student groups in Canvas and automatically created corresponding channels in Slack. Students instantly appeared in both places, and the geek in me enjoyed watching every minute of it.

No-Code and Low-Code Tools

Full-stack engineers use their prodigious coding chops to easily automate tasks, but what about those who don't know a lick of code? Macros are one option, but they're fundamentally limited, as we saw in Table 4.2.

Citizen developers are in luck. Zapier, Make.com, Workato, and IFTTT are just some of the tools that let nontechies automate manual tasks and processes. Think of them as recipes of sorts that can perform multiple steps and even different apps. I cover this subject far deeper in my previous book, *Low-Code/No-Code*.

What Lies Ahead: Lessons From Amazon

Even without increased employee empowerment and inflation, technological advances and economic incentives make more automation inevitable. That much is obvious, but in what ways?

Reading the Amazon Tea Leaves

Here it's instructive to look at the history of Amazon, a company that's been consistently ahead of the curve. Table 4.3 displays a list of some of its most historic innovations and how other companies have responded.

Innovation	Description and Competitor Responses
Cloud computing	Amazon Web Services launched in 2006 without much fanfare. Google, Microsoft, Oracle, and IBM were caught flat-footed. They eventually realized the ginormous size of the market and spent years playing catch-up to AWS.
Voice assistants/ smart speakers	Based on the success of Amazon's Echo product line, other tech giants developed copycat products. Examples include Google Home, Apple's HomePod, and Samsung's Galaxy Home.
Annual subscription programs	Walmart+ represents its attempt to compete with the insanely successful Amazon Prime.
Delivery	Expect your customers to wait five days for their products to arrive? Good luck with that. Just about every large retailer has attempted to replicate Amazon's options for next- and same-day delivery.
Cashier-free checkout	You won't find cashiers at any of the twenty-five Amazon Go stores. Just like with AWS, Amazon is licensing its homegrown technology to retail outlets.[21] It's the ultimate gangster move: turn your operational costs into sources of revenue.

Table 4.3: Major Amazon Innovations

Note the commonalities in Table 4.3. Amazon's competitors have either:

- Attempted to quickly make up ground.
- Aped the Amazon product or service outright.
- Licensed Amazon's core technology.
- Tried a combination of the three.

Has Amazon batted 1.000? Of course not. Table 4.3 omits some doozies, such as its oft-derided Fire Phone.

A foolproof forecasting method doesn't exist, but if you're trying to make predictions around automation, you could do a lot worse than looking inside Amazon. It has long been applying that same automation-driven mindset to other areas of its business. Here's what Bezos had to say on the subject, "The best customer service is if the customer doesn't need to call you, doesn't need to talk to you. It just works."[22]

Automation Begets Additional Automation

After Amazon mastered selling books online, Bezos and company swiftly and aggressively did the same with other products. Why not sell toothpaste, DVDs, CDs, board games, and much more online?

Employees initially decided on the items the company's massive fulfillment centers would stock and the right quantity of each one to purchase. Amazon's *vendor managers* determined, for example, how much Crest or Colgate to order for Phoenix in December. They then manually placed those orders. Note that vendor managers weren't flying blind. Amazon provided them with relevant data to guide those individual decisions.

Starting in 2012, however, Amazon began to minimize the degree of human decision-making involved in this process. The company launched Project Yoda—at first, a way for its algorithms to recommend products and quantities to its vendor managers. In Yoda's early days, employees could override its suggestions. Many did, setting back progress.[23] And that doesn't fly at Amazon.

Alex Kantrowitz is a CNBC contributor and the author of *Always Day One: How the Tech Titans Plan to Stay on Top Forever*. As he described in his Substack:

> Vendor managers' jobs soon changed profoundly. "We were not able to order as much as we used to with the freedom and flexibility that we used to be able to," Elaine Kwon, a former vendor manager, told me. "At some point, if I'm preparing for a big holiday, I spend a lot of my time thinking about what to order. That is a buyer's job, to figure out what to buy. That's slowly getting taken away too. [Management] was like, 'No, we're not going to have you guys do that.'"[24]

Based on its success and lessons learned, Amazon upped the ante with Project Yoda. Its current name is Hands off the Wheel. The company automated an array of tasks, jobs, and even entire functions in its corporate offices. During the pandemic, the company automated nearly all its hiring process for certain positions. Applicants for picker jobs received offers—ready for this?—despite never interacting with a single Amazon employee. In some cases, new hires spent less than five minutes talking to a human being before punching in.[25]

Hardware and Robotics

Amazon has relied upon ultra-sophisticated mobile robots in its fulfillment centers since its 2012 acquisition of Kiva Systems for $775 million.[26] Behind the scenes, who knows if a sentient being packed your USB charger?

Outside of Amazon, expect more public-facing robots like the ones described at the start of this chapter that let customers order Quarter Pounders without speaking to a soul.

卌 IIII

Amazon may represent an extreme comparison or, in your case, an invalid one. Maybe you and I would never hire someone sight unseen. The idea of replacing Tom in Accounting or Greg in Marketing with software or a proper robot might be absurd.

Still, odds are high that automation will replace a good deal of manual work over the next decade and beyond. Tasks, processes, jobs, departments, firms, and even entire industries will either cease to exist or no longer require human hands. Let's hope that we don't automate away half or three-quarters of jobs. As a society, we're simply not prepared for it.

Automation is a powerful force that's quickly gaining momentum. So is its cousin, artificial intelligence—the topic of the next chapter.

Key Points
- A McDonald's in Texas allowed customers to order and pick up meals without any human interaction.
- Robotic process automation and automated testing are just a few of the sophisticated technologies reducing the need for human employees.

- If Amazon is any guide (and it usually is), expect traditional jobs and even entire processes to require less human interaction.
- Successful automation efforts will beget further ones.

CHAPTER 5

Generative AI

Software is getting very creative. Its effects on the workplace will be profound and irreversible.

"Plastics."

—WALTER BROOKE AS MR. MCGUIRE, *THE GRADUATE*

Few scenes from 1960s movies are as iconic in the history of American cinema as the one in Mike Nichols's 1967 film. Dustin Hoffman plays Ben Braddock, a young, disenchanted college graduate. At a party, he regularly hears the same advice from several well-intentioned elders. These sage folks have seen the future, and it's all about plastics.

If Nichols had directed that same flick in 1998, Benjamin would have repeatedly heard wildly different advice. It would be apt to describe the last quarter-century with a single word: technology. Thanks to it, ours is a very different world. It's indisputably better in some ways and worse in others.

Still, some tech events stand out for their importance.

January 23, 1993, saw the launch of Mosaic, the web browser that gave everyday folks access to the internet. No, it wasn't the first of its kind, but it represented a giant leap forward. It popularized webpages, ecommerce, online images, and so much more.

More than five years later, Larry Page and Sergey Brin founded Google on September 4, 1998. AltaVista, Yahoo!, AlltheWeb, AskJeeves, and other search engines cratered. As of January 2022, Google accounted for more than 93 percent of the US mobile search market.[1] You know you've made it big when Webster lists variants of your company name as a verb and an adjective.

Facebook arrived on February 4, 2004. For three years, only college students could technically use the social network. By 2007, the floodgates opened, and the rest is history.

The iPhone arrived on June 29, 2007, portending the end of Nokia phones and Blackberrys. Estimates put the number of iPhones sold as of 2022 at 2.2 billion.[2]

It's still early, but these events may soon pale compared to what happened on November 30, 2022.

Unpacking ChatGPT

Just as we were finishing our Thanksgiving leftovers last year, the American artificial intelligence research laboratory OpenAI released a powerful text-generation tool called ChatGPT. Rather than define it in my own words, I'll get all meta. I'll let ChatGPT introduce itself in Figure 5.1.

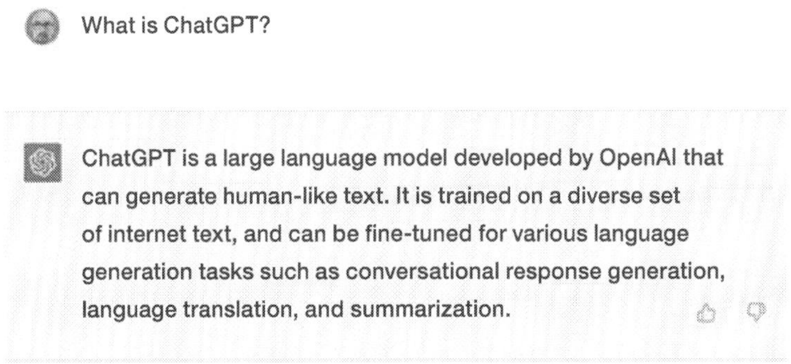

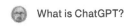
What is ChatGPT?

ChatGPT is a large language model developed by OpenAI that can generate human-like text. It is trained on a diverse set of internet text, and can be fine-tuned for various language generation tasks such as conversational response generation, language translation, and summarization.

Figure 5.1: ChatGPT Defines Itself, Source: OpenAI

ChatGPT is no parlor trick or vaporware. (In case you're curious, this is the only time that I used it while writing this book.*) The sophisticated tool relies upon the latest version of OpenAI's generative pre-trained transformer, version 3.5. A full technical explanation of GPT isn't necessary here. Suffice it to say that it systematically combs through and ingests ginormous amounts of data. It then applies "a machine-learning technique that teaches computers to do what comes naturally to humans: learn by example."[3] We call this *deep learning*.

Again, there's much more to it, but machine learning is a subset of AI. And deep learning is a subset of machine learning. A helpful analogy is Matryoshka or Russian tea dolls, as Figure 5.2 shows on the following page.

If you haven't taken ChatGPT for a test drive yourself yet, I encourage you to do so. You'll quickly understand why its release broke the internet, as the kids say. Twitter was all in a twitter.

---

* For my post on the subject, see https://tinyurl.com/no-chat-for-me.

Unpacking AI

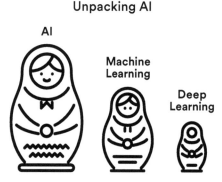

Figure 5.2: Unpacking AI

ChatGPT packed the requisite wow factor to elicit countless reactions from the cognoscenti. Derek Thompson of *The Atlantic* named ChatGPT one of his breakthroughs of 2022. In his words, "These uncanny tools, having emerged from our mind, may change our mind about how we work, how we think, and what human creativity really is."[4]

Cade Metz of the *New York Times* opined, "The Turing test used to be the gold standard for proving machine intelligence. This generation of bots is racing past it."[5]

Dharmesh Shah is the founder and CTO of HubSpot, a company that makes customer relationship management and marketing software. As he astutely observed on LinkedIn, "The Internet existed before Netscape. But the browser helped millions of mere mortals connect the dots on what could be done, and dream of what could be."

It's a valid comparison. Netscape democratized the internet, and ChatGPT is doing that with AI. Within five days of its launch, more than one million people had used it.[6] Figure 5.3 puts that figure into context.

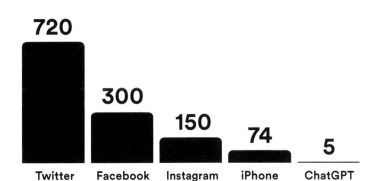

Figure 5.3: Days Needed to Reach One Million Users
Source: OpenAI

Evaluating the Hype

Is all the hype around ChatGPT *really* justified, though? Not everyone is sold.

As OpenAI CEO Sam Altman cautioned over Twitter, "It's a mistake to be relying on ChatGPT for anything important right now."[7] No argument here, but the operative words in that tweet are *right now.*

AI expert Gary Marcus echoes that sentiment. In January 2023, he appeared on *The Prof G Pod with Scott Galloway.* Marcus is the author of several books on the subject and an NYU professor.

Marcus is not nearly as buoyant on the release of ChatGPT as Thompson, Shah, and countless others. In his words, ChatGPT's backbone (version 3.5) is "not so different from a bunch of other systems that came before it,"[8] including:

- **GPT version 3:** The previous iteration that OpenAI launched to a more limited audience in June 2020.

- **Meta's Galactica AI:** Pulled by the company a whole three days after its November 2022 launch because of its obvious inaccuracies.[9]

Despite its fancy tech, Marcus wisely reminds us to remain cautious. ChatGPT is still problematic; most importantly, it can't distinguish fact from fiction. Its results sound more authoritative than they are. Much of the hype stemmed from the scale of OpenAI's 3.5 launch. Version 3 was much more limited.

Not Just Text

As we'll see in this chapter, while GPTs aren't perfect, they can already serve a number of practical business purposes. That is, they can do more than just spit out original, possibly apocryphal text in response to user prompts. ChatGPT sits under a larger group of technologies called *generative AI*. As Kevin Roose of the *New York Times* put it, it's "a wonky umbrella term for AI that doesn't just analyze existing data but creates new text, images, videos, code snippets, and more."[10]

If you're a writer, software developer, graphic designer, photographer, artist, or any other type of creative, that last sentence should give you pause. Yes, AI has been around in different forms for decades. With the launch of ChatGPT, though, AI is no longer some abstract, distant threat. Shit is starting to get real—and fast.

And lest you think that ChatGPT is a one-off project by a single rogue company, let me disabuse you of that notion. AI is a burgeoning field, and generative AI is attracting mad stacks.

Follow the Money

A decent, albeit imperfect, way to predict the future involves following the money. Ask yourself two questions:

- Where are venture capitalists placing their bets?
- How significant are those amounts?

Estimates vary, but here are a few. The Organization for Economic Cooperation and Development reported that the global annual value of VC investments in AI firms in 2020 was $75 billion. In 2012, that number was less than $3 billion.[11]

Figure 5.4 shows an even more precipitous thirty-fold, inflation-adjusted rise over a nine-year period.

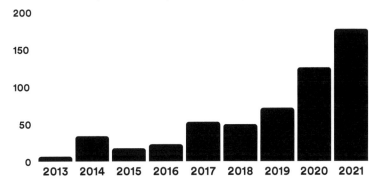

Note: Data is expressed in constant 2021 USD. Inflation adjustment is based on the US Consumer Price Index.

Figure 5.4: Annual Global Corporate Investment in AI 2013–2021
Source: NetBase Quid 2022 AI Index Report

Investors clearly see AI dollar signs, but what about generative AI in particular? The top dogs at the prominent VC firm Sequoia

Capital believe it "has the potential to generate trillions of dollars of economic value."[12] Pitchbook reports that VCs have increased their investment in generative AI by 425 percent since 2020 to $2.1 billion.[13] CB Insights estimates that 110 startups raised $2.6 billion in 2022.[14]

Investors want to make money. Ho hum. But what about the people who are making budgeting and spending decisions? Are they buying into the AI hype?

In short, yes.

In September 2022, the MIT Technology Review released the results of an extensive survey of CIOs and other business leaders. The topics included enterprise systems, AI, and their strategic plans. Here are some interesting findings:

> The surveyed companies' data and AI strategies are close-ly interlinked. Over three-quarters (78%) of the executives we surveyed—and almost all (96%) of the leader group—say that scaling AI and machine learning use cases to create business value is their top priority for enterprise data strategy over the next three years.[15]

Despite the report's stilted language, it's clear that the C-suite increasingly recognizes the vast potential of AI. As for why I suspect that, several forces are at play.

First, as we saw in Chapters 1 through 3, workers are expensive, demanding, and finicky about where they work. Beyond that, AI has matured considerably in recent years. It's become less abstract. Recent advances (such as ChatGPT) have convinced some grizzled skeptics of its capabilities, but don't believe me.

Jasper is an AI copywriting app for marketers. In October 2022, it raised $125 million, valuing the company at $1.5 billion.[16] In the words of cofounder and CEO Dave Rogenmoser, "About two years ago, we realized (AI) had crossed a threshold. It started producing better end results."[17]

And just to put a bow on OpenAI, its valuation stands at $29 billion as of this writing.[18] Expect more AI unicorns in the years ahead.

Generative AI in the Workplace

Anyone today can use a third-party tool with a conversational interface and natural language to churn out decent text. To be sure, ChatGPT is impressive, but does it represent the full extent of generative AI's power?

To quote the immortal John Bender from *Breakfast Club*: not even close, bud.

Generative AI is *already* doing much more. It serves as the backbone for standalone apps and enhances existing ones. Let's peek into its current capabilities.

Image Creation

In January 2021, the same OpenAI released DALL·E, a neural network "that creates images from text captions for a wide range of concepts expressible in natural language."[19] It works similarly to ChatGPT. Just type in a few words and let DALL·E work its magic, as Figures 5.5 and 5.6 display, respectively.

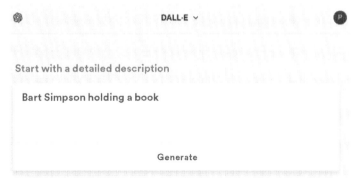

Figure 5.5: DALL·E Prompt, Source: DALL·E

A few seconds later, DALL·E returned the following:

Figure 5.6: DALL·E Results, Source: DALL·E

If you don't feel like typing in words to generate images, just upload a few pics on a similar topic and chill for a few.

In July 2022, OpenAI dropped a beta of its successor, DALL·E 2. Compared to its predecessor, the second iteration generated more realistic and accurate images with four times the resolution. What's more, it "can combine concepts, attributes, and styles."[20]

Note that both DALL·E and DALL·E 2 rely upon the same GPT-3 that underpins ChatGPT. Even as OpenAI released GPT-3, it was already working hard on its successor, GPT-4 (More on this later.) Some AI experts have predicted that GPT-4 will ship with more than 100 trillion parameters—more than 500 times as many as GPT-3.[21]

Brainstorming

Professional scribes, bloggers, and social media types are using ChatGPT to counter an old foe: writer's block.

Paired Programming on Steroids

Walk by the desk of a software engineer at your organization. The odds are high that she's using an integrated development environment. Think of an IDE as a developer's Swiss army knife. It conveniently places all developer programming needs in a single, neat place.

IDEs aren't new. Mainstream ones have shipped with native autocomplete functionality for years or supported third-party plugins that did the same. They work as follows: as developers type their lines of code, autocomplete predicts the text that probably should or usually comes next. This feature does more than just save time. It minimizes errors, interprets them when they occur, and offers relatively basic real-time solutions.

Thanks to generative AI, one mainstream IDE, Visual Studio 2022, is getting much smarter. On March 29, 2022, GitHub announced Copilot. Billed as "your AI pair programmer,"* the tool

---

* In pair programming, Developer #1 (the driver) codes while Developer #2 (the navigator) observes, points out errors, and recommends solutions while hopefully not annoying Developer #1.

"turns natural language prompts into coding suggestions across dozens of languages.[22] Copilot can do this because its creators trained it on billions of lines of code.

Think of it as ChatGPT, but for software developers. As Dave Gershgorn described for The Verge:

> Copilot does more than just parrot back code it's seen before, according to GitHub. It instead analyzes the code you've already written and generates new matching code, including specific functions that were previously called. Examples on the project's website include automatically writing the code to import tweets, draw a scatterplot, or grab a Goodreads rating.[23]

Again, it's not perfect, but it's impressive. Most important, its functionality will improve over time. In case you're wondering, Copilot also relies on GPT-3.

Enhancing Existing Software Applications

Damn coders. Why do they get to have all the fun?

Fortunately, all nontechies will soon be able to benefit from generative AI. Depending on the current situation, you may already be able to take advantage of different generative AI features.

Notion

Notion is a flexible and popular productivity and note-taking tool. (My previous book, *Low-Code/No-Code*, describes some of its manifold uses and my unabashed love of it.) On November 16, 2022, a few days before ChatGPT's public launch, Notion announced that users could access the AI writing assistant within the app.[24] Expect Notion's competitors to add similar functionality.

Canva

For those who don't want to learn Adobe Illustrator and Photoshop, Canva is a user-friendly and affordable alternative. In November 2022, the company added text-to-image capability.[25] It works identically to the other standalone tools mentioned earlier in this chapter. Punch in a few words, and wait for Canva to generate unique images.

Canva Docs represents its foray into rich-text document creation. No, it won't kill proper desktop publishing tools like Adobe InDesign. But it will, I hope, put an end to novices' efforts to create souped-up Microsoft Word documents. To help writers get going, Canva in December 2022 introduced Magic Write, "a magic new copywriting assistant helping you get to your first draft, fast"[26] based on GPT.

Feedly

Feedly is a popular news aggregator. It allows users to consolidate, group, and search newsletters, RSS feeds,* sub Reddits, tweets, and other sources of information automatically. (When Google Reader perished in 2013, a good percentage of its passionate users flocked to Feedly.)

In January 2020, the company launched Leo, billed as "your AI research assistant."[27] Its impressive list of capabilities includes the ability to:

- Prioritize topics, trends, and keywords of interest.
- Deduplicate repetitive news.
- Mute irrelevant information.
- Summarize articles.

---

* An acronym for *really simple syndication.*

The items that users store in Feedly (along with their metadata) allow Leo to learn what's important to them, but it gets even better. Leo suggests content they'd otherwise have missed. Leo and similar tools can improve the scope and quality of a research or writing project while decreasing the time needed to complete it.

Microsoft

Speaking at the 2023 World Economic Forum in Davos, Switzerland, Microsoft CEO Satya Nadella said that his company would soon integrate ChatGPT and other OpenAI tools into all of its products.[28] Maybe PowerPoint will tell you in the future that your slides are too cluttered and create a better presentation for you.

More Intelligent Messages

Opaque and downright inscrutable messages from our computers' operating systems and software programs have frustrated us for years. At some point, you probably saw the "PC Load Letter" error message on your printer and wanted to go all *Office Space* on it.

Generative AI will soon go way beyond providing error messages that we can understand. It will recommend solutions and even implement them automatically. Regardless of what we say or type, AI will be able to infer what *we meant* to do.

Workplace Considerations

The American historian and history professor Melvin Kranzberg once famously opined, "Technology is neither good nor bad; nor is it neutral." As we'll see in this section, nowhere do those words ring truer than with generative AI.

Generative AI is a bit of a Rorschach test. It's not hard to find positives and negatives. Here are some of them.

Productivity

At a high level, generative AI tools may make some workers more productive—in some cases, much more. While researching this book, I came across an interesting analogy of how we'll use tools based on generative AI in the coming years.

Professional golfers walk the course but don't carry their own bags. That job falls to their caddies. These folks do more than just lug heavy bags of clubs, golf balls, snacks, umbrellas, water, and other assorted equipment. They don't just rake sand traps. Before their bosses tee off, caddies meticulously study the course before tournaments begin. While rounds are taking place, they make critical recommendations on where the golfers should aim, which club to hit, and how to read a putt.

Caddies' advice can be indispensable. A single stroke is usually the difference between making and missing the cut, among other things. For their efforts, caddies typically earn $2,000 per week plus anywhere from 5 to 10 percent of their bosses' weekly prize money.[29]

Think of generative AI tools as caddies—at least in the short term. They don't swing the clubs themselves, and they aren't infallible. Caddies' tips help pro golfers hit the best golf shot possible under the circumstances. In other words, the best caddie in and of itself means zilch. All things being equal, however, a better caddie results in a better outcome.

To complete the analogy, robots may swing the clubs themselves in the future, and the golfer may become irrelevant. We're not there yet, though. The arrival of generative AI also means that employers will *try* to get more bang for their employee buck.

Why Increased Productivity Isn't a Given

In 1987, the noted economist Robert Solow wrote in the *New York Times*, "You can see the computer age everywhere but in the productivity statistics."[30]

Thus, the Solow Paradox was born.

In 2023, it remains alive and well. Over the past four decades, we've seen the advent of the World Wide Web, Google, the smartphone, and other flabbergasting technological advances. Despite these arrivals, plenty of the most common productivity measures have largely remained stagnant. In certain EU countries, productivity has even declined.[31]

Should we take it as a given that generative AI will let us do more with less?

No, says Eli Dourado, a senior research fellow at the Center for Growth and Opportunity at Utah State University. As he wrote on his January 2023 Substack, "What if AI ends up like the internet—transformative to our daily lives while somehow not actually delivering major productivity gains? It's worth considering."[32]

General or aggregate trends always mask individual and group differences. Some cohorts will benefit more from generative AI than others. We just don't know which ones yet.

Massive Job Losses?

These newfangled generative AI tools are exciting and more than a little addictive. (The phrase *time suck* comes to mind.) Some might see them as innocuous. For example, let's examine image-generation programs. What's the harm in creating a few goofy images like Bart Simpson holding a book?

In October 2022, I hired a local photographer to take a few headshots. I wanted to spruce up my website and add a more recent pic to the back of my book *Low-Code/No-Code*. I spent a modest $120 for 50 pictures, one of which adorns the physical book.

Could AI have done the same?

Yes.

The AI portrait app Lensa launched in 2018 and performed respectably. That is, it caught lightning in a bottle à la Instagram in 2010. In late 2022, Lensa soared in popularity after its newly launched magic avatar feature went viral.[33] At that time, I downloaded it for my iPhone. I ordered fifty original AI-generated images for a whopping total of $3. After uploading eight existing headshots, Lensa spit out its creations. I didn't care much for Lensa's depiction of me in space, but some of its photos were pretty slick. Figure 5.7 shows a few of them.

Figure 5.7: Lensa App Results

Will proper photographers go the way of travel agents? What about knowledge workers, like lawyers?

Erik Brynjolfsson is the director of the Stanford Digital Economy Lab and a professor there to boot. As he told David Pogue on *CBS Sunday Morning* in January 2023:

> If done right, it's not going to be AI replacing lawyers. It's going to be lawyers working with AI replacing lawyers who don't work with AI.[34]

Or, while we're at it, what about entire mega-corporations?

Some industry types have speculated that tools like ChatGPT may soon obviate search engines.[35] Google, as we know it, could become another AskJeeves. The juggernaut typically generates about $150 billion yearly for its parent company, Alphabet. That number represents more than 80 percent of Alphabet's annual revenue.[36] Will people use ChatGPT instead of Google? If they do, they won't click on ads—at least on Google's ads.

The idea that search engines may evaporate seems unlikely. Still, search just became far more interesting than it has been in twenty years. In early February 2023 Microsoft announced that it had already started integrating OpenAI's tech into Bing, its also-ran search engine. Early reviews from beta testers were positive. Johanna Stern of the *Wall Street Journal* wrote that "search will never be the same."[37] Odds are that Bing will capture a good chunk of its rival's 84 percent market share.[38]

Google's head honchos are too smart to sit back as Bing generates buzz. What's more, the company hasn't exactly been ignoring AI. Recall Ian Goodfellow from Chapter 2, the machine learning expert who bolted Apple for Google's DeepMind after the former ordered him back to work. As I was wrapping up the manuscript for this book, Google launched Bard, its ChatGPT competitor.[39]

Stay tuned.

Objectionable Content

I covered DALL·E and DALL·E 2 earlier in this chapter, but plenty of other AI image generators exist. Examples include Craiyon (formerly DALL·E mini) and Midjourney. The one that has arguably garnered the most press, however, is Stable Diffusion. Anyone can visit the code repository GitHub, download Stable Diffusion, and tweak its source code.[40] Some techies have released forked versions and removed Stable Diffusion's safety filter. Predictably, some have used the uncensored versions to "make freaky, machine-generated porn"[41] and flood Reddit boards with its gruesome images.

Yikes.

Deepfakes

Pulling a fast one on your boss or college professor is one thing, but what about creating a fictitious video or audio recording of her?

The tools to do these things exist, and not just for hackers surfing the Dark Web.

In July 2021, *Roadrunner*, a movie about the late chef Anthony Bourdain, appeared in theaters. While doing press to support its release, director Morgan Neville admitted using "voice-cloning software to make the late chef Anthony Bourdain say words he never spoke.[42] The admission resulted in a maelstrom of criticism.

Better Call Saul?

Even if those qualms don't bother you, consider the potential legal issues stemming from remixing others' copyrighted images.

Say that you use Stable Diffusion to create, um, adult caricatures of Mickey and Minnie Mouse for a risqué marketing campaign. Legally speaking, are you good?

I'm no lawyer, but the answer is certainly not an unequivocal *yes*. If Disney's legal department happens across your artistic creations, you may be in for a world of pain:

> The Disney Group takes Disney trademark infringement seriously and has copyright and trademark registrations to protect its characters. Anyone who wants to use the characters from the Disney franchise must follow all legal requirements to avoid infringing on the company's intellectual property rights.[43]

Artists regularly question the ethics of using AI to further their creative endeavors.[44] Is it a stretch to think that some won't call attorneys when others appropriate their creations?

It's already happening.

A trio of artists filed a lawsuit against two makers of image generation tools: Stability AI and Midjourney.[45] As James Vincent wrote on The Verge, the individuals:

> allege that these organizations have infringed the rights of 'millions of artists' by training their AI tools on five billion images scraped from the web 'without the consent of the original artists.'

Stability AI faces a separate suit from stock photo site Getty Images for scraping its content.[46]

Vincent summed up the issue succinctly in a separate piece: "The scary truth about AI copyright is nobody knows what will happen next."[47] You're on far safer legal ground by avoiding some generative AI tools altogether. You won't end up in court if you commission an artist to produce original drawings and designs. Go old school, baby.

Perhaps potential legal issues are preventing Google from releasing its new tool that allows users to generate music from text descriptions.[48]

Questionable Decisions

Certain applications have earned our trust over time. We're confident that Microsoft Excel correctly analyzes data, calculates averages, and produces charts. Our email messages arrive unaltered.

We still need to use our brains. For example, it's dangerous to blindly trust Google results without reviewing the source of its recommendations.

And there's this crop of powerful, yet largely unproven generative AI tools. The algorithms work their magic in black boxes and provide zero transparency into their methods. The word *opaque* comes to mind. Are you willing to let them make key business or life decisions? Should we effectively represent their results as our original creations?

I'm not.

Fraud and Deception

High school and college students have started using generative AI to generate unique essays and writing assignments that anti-plagiarism checkers can't detect. Universities are scrambling to develop policies and deploy technologies to thwart them.[49]

Tired of showing up at Zoom meetings as yourself? Avatarify is a free program that lets users superimpose another person's face onto theirs during videoconferences. Want to noodle with it? Knock yourself out on GitHub.[50]

Maybe you want to blow off the weekly departmental meeting altogether. It's not hard to create a custom Zoom background that makes it appear that you're attentively listening to your colleagues when you're doing anything but.[51]

Going Too Fast Too Soon

With any emerging technology, strong incentives exist to exaggerate its capabilities, especially among the ethically challenged. Case in point: a certain electric-car company. Multiple lawsuits "argue that Tesla's self-driving software is dangerously overhyped."[52] Tellingly, Musk initially vetoed his team's preferred name of *Copilot*, insisting upon *Autopilot*. In July 2023, *Bloomberg* reported that "Musk oversaw the faked 2016 Autopilot video."[53]

Musk's penchant for hyperbole and showmanship rivals that of P. T. Barnum, but he's hardly the only source of embellishment.

Since 1994, CNET has been a popular website that has published thousands of articles about technology and consumer electronics. Its current tagline reads, "Your guide to a better future." Evidently, that future doesn't include fact-checking.

The site has begun quietly using AI to generate original content. As of this writing, CNET Money has penned seventy-three articles,[54] and it's "already publishing very dumb errors."[55] (Maybe it should steal a page from the Associated Press's playbook. The AP has been using robot journalists to write limited financial articles since at least 2015 sans the same level of controversy.[56])

The dangers of eliminating all human supervision from creative endeavors today are obvious—or at least they should be to responsible business leaders. In this case, CNET loses credibility with discerning readers in an already challenging environment. (How long until advertisers follow?) Those unable or unwilling to fact-check CNET'S claims proceed with false knowledge that, as George Bernard Shaw famously said, is more dangerous than ignorance. Let's hope that management at BuzzFeed and other sites heed Shaw's warning as they use ChatGPT to churn out quick and cheap content.[57]

Predictions

Peering into the future of any emerging technology is a roll of the dice. History has repeatedly shown that predictions aren't guarantees, even from folks in the know. In the early 1940s, IBM's President Thomas J. Watson opined, "I think there is a world market for about five computers."[58] After the 2007 launch of the iPhone, Microsoft's then-CEO famously said, "There's no chance that the iPhone is going to get any significant market share. No chance." Long-defunct AltaVista could have bought Google in 1998 for a mere $1 million.[59]

Whoops.

It's entirely possible that the AI bulls are misguided. Former US Treasury Secretary Larry Summers's admittedly tempered comparison of AI to historical game-changers may be wildly inaccurate:

> Just as the printing press or electricity was a huge change because it was a general-purpose technology, this could be the most important general-purpose technology since the wheel or fire. And that is something we all are going to be changed by.[60]

I can't fathom how all the AI advancements and billions invested will result in bupkis. With respect to generative AI, the essential question isn't *if* sophisticated tools will transform the workplace. The better questions are *when* and *how*.

When Not If

What will happen with AI?

The rise of cloud computing is an instructive historical parallel here. For more than a decade, millions of businesses have been able to access affordable, flexible, and robust compute power via Amazon Web Services, Google Cloud, Microsoft Azure, and others.

Servers have effectively become utilities like water and electricity. The shift has allowed countless companies to exit the IT business. They reallocated scarce resources to more strategic and differentiated areas of their businesses. Although it won't happen tomorrow, expect the same thing to take place with generative AI.

Let's ponder the insights of big-tech journalist Alex Kantrowitz, whom we met in the previous chapter. In his words:

> This commitment to AI in the workplace is newly relevant as powerful tools like DALL·E, ChatGPT, and their ilk make their way into the public's hands. As access to this powerful technology spreads, nearly all companies will soon have tools like those I saw inside Amazon, Apple, Facebook, Google, and Microsoft. So, work inside our companies will change as well.[61]

When it comes to AI, the big questions include:

- Which companies will first provide the services?
- When will we be able to use them?

Thanks to its partnership with OpenAI, Microsoft appears to be in the lead. Don't count out Amazon, though. (Review Table 4.3 if you forgot how frequently Amazon has beat its competitors to market.)

GPT-4 Concurrently Amazes and Disappoints

On March 14, 2023, OpenAI announced the launch of the next iteration of GPT. Of course, it represented an improvement over its predecessors, but will it live up to its considerable hype?

The answer is *yes*. More than one thing can be true.

Here's what OpenAI CEO Sam Altman said about GPT-4: "People are begging to be disappointed and they will be."[62] In January 2023, he refused to confirm that his organization would even release it in the coming year.

Generative AI technology will nevertheless march onward and improve along the way. This force will only accelerate in the coming years. The list, variety, and quality of these tools will continue to grow.* Eli Dourado smartly observes, "Today's models are the worst that they will ever be—they will only get better from here."[63]

The general trend is easy to predict, but it's silly to pretend to know *exactly* how AI will ultimately play out. The cartoon in Figure 5.8 cleverly illustrates as much.

---

* See https://www.gpt-list.com.

© marketoonist.com

Figure 5.8: AI Cartoon

Hiring Matters

In a way, generative AI changes nothing. Doing more with less will continue to rule the day. That's the nature of capitalism.

Along with the other forces in this book, generative AI will prove too tempting to resist. Plenty of firms will cut back on hiring. Bosses will expect their employees to wear multiple hats. Why can't a graphic designer also serve as a copywriter or blogger? Our financial analyst is an Excel wiz. Surely, he can build our website and manage our social media accounts in his spare time, right?

This mindset is misguided. The world's best golf caddies don't also do side hustles as tennis coaches. The jack of all trades is the master of none.

Some companies will use generative AI to aggressively supplant people with machines and software. But firms that eliminate the human element will regret it. Generative AI just isn't there yet. What's more, morale among existing employees will crater.

Finally, more companies will hire fractional legal counsels specifically to handle a burgeoning array of complicated AI issues. (Chapter 9 returns to this subject.)

Key Points

- To knowledge workers and creatives, AI has always been an existential threat, albeit a distant and abstract one. ChatGPT made it much more concrete.
- Practical and legal considerations make going all-in on AI unwise at this time. Fine, but it's silly to ignore it altogether.
- Major software applications and suites will integrate generative AI tools. In fact, this is already happening.
- Generative AI will continue to make tremendous strides. It's nowhere near the point of eliminating the need for human oversight, however.

CHAPTER 6

Blockchain

Trust is rapidly evaporating, and the revolutionary technology could not have arrived at a better time.

"Trust, but verify."

—RONALD REAGAN

In December 2022, Gustavo Miller saw a position as a digital marketing manager at the cryptocurrency exchange Coinbase. He was intrigued.

The Lisbon, Portugal, resident was keen on remote positions. He applied and soon received an email from a Coinbase recruiter about scheduling an online interview.

The conversation went well, and Miller received a formal employment offer the day before Christmas. He accepted, signed the offer letter, and then received an introductory email from the company. That message contained a link to Bitrix24, an online workspace for small, medium, and large businesses.

In his LinkedIn post[1] detailing his travails, Miller described his first day of employment as "normal, the second day not so much." Coinbase had him install Paxful, a peer-to-peer wallet that would let him buy and sell Bitcoin. His new Coinbase manager asked him to use it to purchase $200 of the volatile cryptocurrency.

There was just one problem, though.

No actual Coinbase employee had communicated with him. It was a scam.

Tech-savvy Miller caught on quickly. All things considered, he shouldn't feel too bad. First, although he wasted some time, Miller didn't remit to the scammers the $3,200 in Bitcoin that Coinbase allegedly wanted him to spend on equipment for his new, er, job. Second, he achieved a bit of notoriety. His LinkedIn post went viral, generating more than 11 million impressions as of this writing and an appearance in this book.

Maybe his honest post about the experience will help others avoid similar fates. As he wrote:

> These scammers know how to target vulnerable people and swindle them. I felt really stupid and naïve when I discovered it, but I know this is not a silly scam. These guys are pro, they know the standard remote-first jobs conditions and the tech industry's hiring culture.[2]

The data bears out Miller's claim. He may live in Portugal, but untold others have fallen victim to similar schemes. According to the Federal Trade Commission:

The number of reported job scams nearly tripled to
104,000 between 2019 and 2021 and remained elevated in 2022. US workers lost more than $200 million from
employment-related scams in 2021, up from $133 million
in 2019, agency data show.[3]

Cons involving remote jobs may be relatively new, but people
have been falsifying professional credentials for centuries. Allow
me to present Exhibit A. After a brief five-month stint as CEO of
Yahoo! in 2012, Scott Thompson resigned in disgrace. Word broke
that he hadn't, as his resume stated, received his undergraduate
degree in computer science.[4]

Returning to Europe for a moment, UK authorities finally realized in January 2023 that psychiatrist Zholia Alemi had been prac-
ticing with a bogus medical degree for more than twenty years.
The "most accomplished forger and fraudster" allegedly fooled the
General Medical Council into granting her registration as a doctor. Alemi then worked for a slew of health trusts across the UK.[5]

Let's take it up a notch and discuss a costlier (alleged)
deception.

In September 2021, JPMorgan Chase acquired Frank, "the
fastest growing college financial planning platform, to help millions of students and their families navigate their financial journey to college and beyond."[6] From the former's accompanying
press release:

"We want to build lifelong relationships with our customers," said Jennifer Piepszak, co-CEO of Chase. "Frank
offers a unique opportunity for deeper engagement
with students. Together, we'll be able to expand our capabilities for students and their families, helping them

financially prepare for college and other major moments in their future."[7]

The price tag: A bawdy $175 million.

Less than eighteen months later, the financial behemoth shut down the Frank website and filed suit, accusing its founder, Charlie Javice, of fabricating four million fake accounts. As CNBC reported, JPMorgan:

> learned the truth about Frank after sending out marketing e-mails to a batch of 400,000 customers. About 70 percent of the e-mails bounced back, the bank said in a lawsuit filed last month in federal court.[8]

Through his lawyers, Javice denied any wrongdoing. (Number of people surprised: zero.) Lawyers, judges, and the courts will sort out the matter over the coming months and years.

ⅢⅢ ⅢⅢ

These stories make the rounds on traditional and social media. They exacerbate our trust in government, public institutions, business leaders, and each other. That lack of faith complicates solving critical social and economic issues, even making them impossible.[9]

If only there were a way for all parties to be completely confident in their online communications and transactions.

Oh, wait. There is.

It's called *blockchain*.

To be fair, no single tool or technology can immediately restore societal trust. (Dare to dream, right?) Blockchain is no exception to this rule. At a minimum, though, it can significantly minimize fraud and give us more confidence that what we view online is real. As we'll see in this chapter, that's just the tip of the blockchain iceberg.

Let's explore.

A Ridiculously Simple Overview of Blockchain

The roots of blockchain trace back four decades and involve cryptography. What we now call *blockchain* remained a relatively esoteric, largely academic subject until 2008. That year, Satoshi Nakamoto* published what turned out to be an über-influential white paper, "Bitcoin: A Peer-to-Peer Electronic Cash System."[10]

Bitcoin and blockchain technology arrived simultaneously. As a result, it's easy to erroneously conflate the two. Make no mistake, though: blockchain does much more than underpin a volatile cryptocurrency. (Note that, although Nakamoto conceived of a block of timestamped items, his opus includes nary a single use of the word *blockchain*.) Beyond bitcoin and cryptocurrencies in general, blockchain makes other types of applications possible. We'll tackle some of the most promising— and quite frankly, necessary—ones later in this chapter.

Some smart cookies have argued that blockchain—not Bitcoin—will ultimately prove to be Nakamoto's lasting legacy.[11] By way of background, the digital currencies that predated Bitcoin needed to be centralized to some extent because they suffered from the *double-spend problem*. A central and trusted third party needed to ensure that the tender's owner—or others, for that matter—couldn't spend that same digital cash multiple times.

---

* Probably a pseudonym for an individual or small group. No one knows.

(Physical currency doesn't face this problem. Once you hand the Starbucks barista a $5 bill in exchange for your mochaccino, the Abe Lincoln is no longer yours.)

Blockchain's clever use of mathematics, technology, and cryptography solved the double-spend problem *and* eliminated the need for third-party involvement. It's fully *decentralized*. Blockchain eliminates friction, yet provides extraordinary, nearly immediate transparency into the transactions that take place on it.

Ledgers

Definitions of blockchain are a dime a dozen. Interestingly, just about all of them use the word *ledger*. If you took an accounting class in high school or college or have ever balanced your checkbook, you're already familiar with the concept. In case you aren't, here's a simple example.

Say that you own a small electronics store. You advertise on Google as so many businesses do. On February 1, 2023, Google sends you an invoice for $2,000, due at the end of the month. To keep your books balanced, the transactions in your accounting software ought to look something like the ones in Figure 6.1.

Of course, these transactions need to balance. Whether you use QuickBooks or the horribly named Oracle Fusion Cloud Financials, total debits must equal total credits. If there's a discrepancy, your accounting program will reject the transaction. In this example, the accounting ledger logs all the activity entered. Profit and loss statements, trial balances, and all other financial reports will accurately reflect these transactions.

Simple Accounting Transactions

Date	Account	Debit	Credit
2/1/23	Advertising Expense	$2,000	
2/1/23	Accounts Payable		$2,000
2/28/23	Accounts Payable	$2,000	
2/28/23	Checking Account		$2,000
Totals		$4,000	$4,000

Figure 6.1: Simple Accounting Transactions

But what if you made a mistake? In Figure 6.1, say that you meant to type in $1,000 as the advertising expense. You can easily fix that by entering manual adjustments or simply deleting the original transactions and starting again.*

Blockchain Basics

With that necessary overview of ledgers out of the way, let's continue. In their book *The Truth Machine: The Blockchain and the Future of Everything*, Paul Vigna and Michael J. Casey offer this helpful definition:

> In essence, the blockchain is a digital ledger that's shared across a decentralized network of independent computers, which update and maintain it in a way that allows anyone to prove the record is complete and uncorrupted.

There's a lot to unpack in that sentence. First, as mentioned earlier, blockchain databases are almost always decentralized.

---

* I opt for the latter when I err.

Contrast it to the centralized databases that most organizations use to store vast amounts of user, employee, and customer data. Hackers go after these targets precisely because they contain so much valuable information. Think of it as a bunch of cash in a single safe.

Blockchain's decentralized nature makes it fundamentally more secure than its centralized counterparts. To continue with the banking metaphor, think of blockchain as the equivalent of small amounts of cash stored in safe-deposit boxes in hundreds of banks across the world. Its inherent design makes it far less attractive to black hats.

Data Storage

Blockchain stores data chronologically. Each block concurrently links to the previous and next ones on a sequential chain.[*] (Hence the name.) Complex and shared mathematical algorithms called *hashes* secure that chain. Figure 6.2 shows a simple three-block chain.

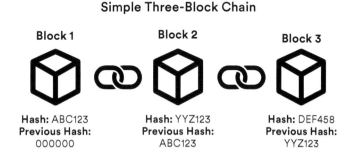

Figure 6.2: Simple Three-Block Chain

---

[*] The only exceptions are the first and the last blocks. The first cannot link to a previous one; the last cannot link to a subsequent one.

Blockchains add new blocks via one of the following two methods:

- **Proof of Work:** In this original approach, *miners* compete to validate transactions and add new blocks to the blockchain.
- **Proof of Stake:** This updated technique is growing in popularity because it's more secure and uses less energy than its antecedent. Randomly selected *validators* confirm transactions and create new blocks.

Regardless of the method involved, there's no practical limit to the number of blocks a chain can store. That's important because blockchain is an append-only ledger. Fixing mistakes requires adding *new* records; no one can delete or alter previous ones. Third parties can neither monitor nor interfere with transactions.

There's much more to it, but I only wanted to provide a concise overview of blockchain technology. Books like *The Truth Machine* go into far greater technical detail.

From Theory to Practice

Most people don't realize that blockchain underpins a particular application, system, or protocol. That's precisely the point. It's unintrusive. It works invisibly, seamlessly, and securely behind the scenes.

In all likelihood, you've already used blockchain technology. You probably just didn't realize it. Someone has most likely sent you a legal document to sign at some point—and not as a PDF attached to an email.

eSignatures

When the commercial arrived circa 1995, few people grasped its profound implications. Within a few years, Amazon ushered in the era of ecommerce. Skype and Vonage embraced voice over internet protocol, obviating the need for people to fork over $1/minute for long-distance and international calls. (Believe it or not, that was a thing.)

By the same token, why spend $50 on FedEx or UPS to obtain an overnight *physical* signature? That's what Tom Gonser, Court Lorenzini, and Eric Ranft thought before launching DocuSign in 2003.

Note that DocuSign's former leadership eschewed blockchain. As former CEO Daniel Springer told John Detrixhe of Quartz in December 2020, "Blockchain is still too expensive for the kinds of things his company does."[12] Maybe that's true, but I suspect that new CEO Allan Thygesan and his lieutenants are keeping close tabs on its evolution.

Some of DocuSign's newer competitors began their ventures with blockchain as a foundational technology. DocHub, founded in 2014, uses blockchain technology "for perpetual verification, as well as snapshots of the document to capture every major change by different entities."[13]

ZorroSign, Zoho Sign, and HelloSign (recently rebranded as Dropbox Sign) have also embraced blockchain tech. Put simply, it makes a great deal of sense. Figure 6.3 shows the transactions behind a HelloSign contract stored on a blockchain.

And we're just getting started. As it turns out, blockchain is making inroads in all sorts of areas.

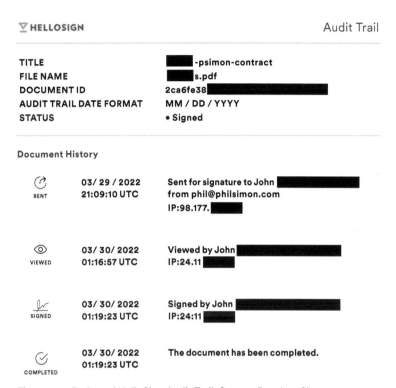

Figure 6.3: Redacted HelloSign Audit Trail, Source: Dropbox Sign

Credentialing and Recruiting

Research from the World Economic Forum in 2017 suggests that the half-life of a professional skill is just five years.[14] It's hard to imagine that number increasing, especially given the rapid AI advances taking place. That same year, "one in four adults reported a mismatch between the skills they have and the skills they need for their current job."[15]

The idea that you'll learn in four years of college everything you need to succeed in life has always been questionable at best. Against a backdrop of rapid change, however, it's downright laughable. College presidents are increasingly glomming on to this notion of *lifetime learning*. They're not wrong. Whether in a formal university setting or not, we need to consistently learn new skills if we want to stay employable.

Plenty of institutions and organizations outside of higher education have moved quickly to meet this demand. The Project Management Institute is one of them. PMI offers dozens of certifications around project management, citizen development, and other topics.[16] Prices range from $79 to hundreds of dollars.

Fantastic, but what good is a credential to a worker who can't *prove* that she legitimately earned it?

Enter Credly, a company that creates, issues, and manages digital credentials using (what else?) blockchain. Individuals who earn valuable professional certificates and badges can opt to publish these *verified* accomplishments on a public blockchain. Recruiters, hiring managers, and anyone else for that matter can see that they have legitimately acquired these formal credentials. Proof of these certs should help them land interviews and new jobs.

Event Attendance

Did you really attend that online sexual harassment training? What about that conference breakout session? Can you *prove* that you didn't just blow it off?

POAP Inc. makes a blockchain-based proof-of-attendance protocol. Through it, a company issues non-fungible tokens that prove when people have attended in-person and virtual events. POAP then sends these digital stickers or badges to users' wallets as attendance rewards. Spotify, Budweiser, Citi, and Goldman Sachs are among the companies that use it.

Supply Chains

As blockchain technology matures, more organizations are realizing its potential applications and benefits and applying it to inefficient and complex areas of their businesses. Supply chains are prime candidates. Blockchain can increase efficiency and speed while concurrently minimizing costly inventory and parts disruptions.

As Vishal Gaur and Abhinav Gaiha write on HBR:

> When blockchain record keeping is used, assets such as units of inventory, orders, loans, and bills of lading are given unique identifiers, which serve as digital tokens (similar to bitcoins). Additionally, participants in the blockchain are given unique identifiers, or digital signatures, which they use to sign the blocks they add to the blockchain. Every step of the transaction is then recorded on the blockchain as a transfer of the corresponding token from one participant to another.[17]

The advantages aren't just theoretical; the technology has matured quite a bit over the past decade. Examples of companies that have used blockchain to gain valuable insights into their complex supply chains include:

- **Emerson:** A multinational manufacturing and engineering company.[18]
- **Hayward:** An international manufacturer of swimming pool equipment.

Remember how blockchain solves the double-spend problem that plagued previous forms of digital cash? In a similar manner, it can prevent manufacturing systems from incorrectly assigning the same unit of capacity or inventory to two different orders.

And it's not just companies that stand to benefit by adopting blockchain technology in manufacturing. Consumers can too.

Take ethical sourcing. Before pulling out their credit cards, people frequently want to know that companies are sourcing their products in an environmentally friendly way. A January 2019 Nielsen survey revealed that nearly three-quarters of global consumers say they would "definitely or probably" change their consumption behavior to reduce their environmental impact.[19] Other recent polls have reflected similar sentiments.

Blockchain can provide unprecedented transparency into a product's provenance. Socially and environmentally conscious consumers can select products that, for example, didn't rely upon child labor to come to market. If that means slightly higher prices, so be it.

Healthcare

In 2021, the US spent more than $12,000 per person on healthcare—the highest per-capita figure across the OECD countries.[20] You'd think that, for that much cabbage, Americans would generally be satisfied with its outcomes.

And you'd be spectacularly wrong.

Despite spending so much, Americans generally hate their healthcare.

As but one recent example, let's examine a September 2022 poll from the Associated Press-NORC Center for Public Affairs Research. Public satisfaction with the US healthcare system is pitiful. Fewer than half of Americans reported holding a favorable opinion of it. Only one in eight believe that it's handled extremely well or very well.[21]

Inefficiency is damn near everywhere. Experts estimate that one-third of healthcare expenditures are inefficient.[22]

Here's my biggest bugaboo: the idea of a new patient manually completing paper forms in a doctor's office. It's absurd, and it has been for years. It astounds me that the process remains so prevalent. (As a rule of thumb, if a business hasn't changed in the past decade, disruption is inevitable.)

Healthcare startups are working on patient blockchains—in effect, secure, digital, and comprehensive medical histories of each vaccine, doctor's appointment, hospitalization, and the like. Patients could easily share this information with existing and future doctors.

Sign me up.

Real Estate

Much like core aspects of healthcare, the process of buying or selling a home hasn't changed all that much. Each is time-consuming, inefficient, and antiquated, and I'm hardly the only one who feels this way.

Sensing opportunity, Zillow management attempted to build a better mousetrap. The company launched Offers in December 2019, starting with markets in Southern California.[23] Swaths of data and complex algorithms would *automatically* make home purchases.

It didn't work; in fact, it was an utter disaster. In November 2021, Zillow laid off two thousand employees and shuttered Zillow Offers. The company also wrote off more than $500 million.

Despite Zillow's failure, the opportunity to improve the home buying experience is massive. Most relevant here, blockchain technology could work wonders. What's more, it could give the staid, fragmented, and protectionist industry the kick in the ass it so desperately needs.

For starters, "traditional methods of property ownership registration are often vulnerable to fraud and errors."[24] Blockchain can store deed-related information in a far more secure and reliable way than paper, spreadsheets, and legacy systems. Its deployment can eliminate manual errors while thwarting fraud and sophisticated property scams.

Smart contracts represent another powerful use of blockchain technology. They automatically execute when it detects that the parties met predetermined terms and conditions. Although it's still early, smart contracts are already automating manual tasks required to complete real estate transactions. Title searches and escrow services most readily come to mind. Costs also drop as costly intermediaries disappear. Finally, blockchain lays the foundation for fractional real estate ownership. (Chapter 9 returns to this subject.)

The tantalizing possibilities don't stop there.

You and your significant other fall in love with a nineteenth century colonial just outside of Boston. You're contemplating making an offer, but something about the home rubs both of you the wrong way.

Did the current owner really replace the air conditioning unit seven years ago? What about the roof? Is it the original one? When exactly were those floors replaced? What other repairs or enhancements did the couple make to their home since they bought it?

Faking vendor invoices isn't hard to do in the era of Photoshop. Even if those contractor bills are legit, investigating repairs and enhancements takes time. What if you could easily audit and verify all the information about your future home? Would you like to be absolutely sure of its entire history *before* plunking down $800,000?

Preventing or Minimizing Fraud

Let's briefly return to the examples at the start of this chapter. Can blockchain technology prevent similar frauds from occurring in the future?

Gustavo Miller

The digital marketing manager could insist upon viewing coming offer letters on a digital signature tool. (Refer to Figure 6.3.) He will then be able to see if a company's alleged recruiters lack proper company email addresses. If the recruiter fails to provide this essential documentation, it will be a major red flag.

Zholia Alemi

The agencies that hire future psychiatrists and practitioners could contract companies like Credly to verify credentials. Alleged MDs who can't produce verified degrees, certificates, and badges won't even be able to apply for open positions.

JPMorgan Chase

Creating bogus accounts is easy for those who possess the programming chops. YouTube is rife with videos of Python wizzes creating hundreds of them in seconds to confound spammers.

As part of its due diligence for future acquisitions and partnerships, leadership can insist upon viewing a random sample of accounts. If new ones aren't created on the blockchain, JPM's compliance folks should just move on. The burnt hand teaches best.

Forces Collide

The forces in this book are colliding with each other. Nowhere is this more evident than with blockchain.

Investor Enthusiasm

As the previous section illustrated, blockchain is an enormously powerful and disruptive force. Beaucoup bucks have poured into startups with creative ideas to take advantage of it.

The numbers are astonishing. Over the thirteen-month period beginning in August 2021, Cointelegraph Research reported that venture capital firms poured nearly $50 billion into blockchain ventures.[25] Figure 6.4 shows the breakdown.

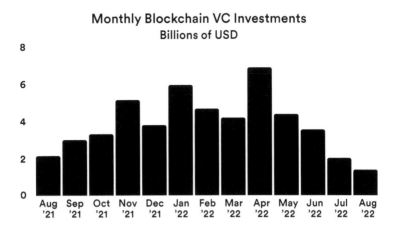

Figure 6.4: Monthly Blockchain VC Investments, Source: Cointelegraph Research

Yes, the number has dropped off. (When you reach $7 billion in a single month, it's hard to go up.) Much of the decline undoubtedly stems from the crypto winter and the rise in interest rates to combat inflation.

Perhaps the most prominent investor banging the blockchain drum is Marc Andreessen. The venture capitalist and cocreator of the first popular web browser, Netscape, in 2016 called it "the distributed trust network that the Internet always needed and never had."[26] His firm Andreessen Horowitz has invested nearly $8 billion in blockchain, cryptocurrency, and other web3* startups.[27]

Inertia

Given blockchain's disruptive nature, it should be no surprise that plenty of entrenched commercial interests aren't exactly hopping on board. Your average fifty- or sixty-something CEO of a healthcare system, insurance company, commercial bank, or real estate franchise wants to maintain the status quo. After all, retirement isn't that far away.

Your average CIO faces similar predicaments. Yeah, the organization's current systems might be a tad dated, but that's no reason to mess around with newfangled and unproven technologies. Events like the $32 billion collapse of FTX in November 2022 and the arrest of founder Sam Bankman-Fried make hidebound executives even less likely to rock the boat.

If it ain't broke, don't fix it, right?

It's an understandable sentiment that students of business history have heard before.

---

* The term means different things to different people. For now, think of *web3* as a decentralized alternative to the web's current incarnation—one with Google, Amazon, Meta, and powerful corporations at the center.

In the late 1990s, the commercial web took root. Amazon, eBay, Cisco, AOL, Priceline, Yahoo!, and other new economy companies sported stratospheric stock prices that confounded traditionalists and their historical models. Did eyeballs and clicks now matter more than bread-and-butter profits and cash flow?

As it turned out, the answer was a resounding *no*. By October 2002, the tech-heavy Nasdaq had fallen 78 percent from its March 2000 peak. Pets.com, Webvan, and dozens of other startups that had just dropped millions on amusing Super Bowl commercials went *poof!* Former Wall Street darlings looked to be acquired, often at a fraction of their previous valuations.

The dot-com crash left old-school executives feeling vindicated, albeit temporarily. People would *always* want to book their vacations through travel agencies, buy their books and music in brick-and-mortar stores, and rent their videos at their local Blockbuster and Hollywood Video stores.

Those same executives are now the punchlines of jokes and the subjects of unflattering MBA case studies.

Predictions

Blockchain will soon cross the chasm, to borrow the title of Geoffrey Moore's 1991 bestseller. The innovators and early adopters have been putting it into practice for years. Soon the early majority will start dipping its toes in the water. It's only a matter of time.

Companies that adopt blockchain will invariably see their workplaces change in profound ways. Efficient, largely automated business processes will replace clunky, manual, and antiquated ones. As we saw in the previous section, blockchain can significantly increase transparency. We'll be able to spot hidden inefficiencies and redundancies. We'll quickly find and curtail waste. AI will detect patterns that we miss and recommend innovative solutions and improvements.

Lessons From 3D Printing

Maybe all those spammy emails from consulting firms and software vendors have made you skeptical about new enterprise technologies. I get it. For example, not long ago, everyone was crooning about 3D printing.

What happened there?

Yes, the early hype around additive manufacturing was deafening. As the technology has matured, though, it's rapidly made inroads into conventional manufacturing across the globe.[28]

3D printing is making rapid inroads into conventional manufacturing all over the world, but it's still nascent. Again, the data bears this out. See Figure 6.5.

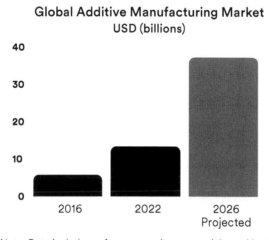

Global Additive Manufacturing Market
USD (billions)

Note: Data includes software, services, materials, and hardware.

Figure 6.5: Global Additive Manufacturing Market, Source: Context

Given the geopolitical and supply chain issues discussed in Chapter 3, the 2026 estimate may well turn out to be conservative.

Blockchain Will Drastically Alter the Workplace

Returning to the subject of this chapter, blockchain's effect on workers and the workplace will be profound—eventually. It will free millions from the tedium of manual, administrative, but currently necessary work. Compared to now, employees will spend a fraction of their current time and energy on the following:

- Tracking down critical information.
- Verifying candidate backgrounds, licenses, and other facts.
- Attempting to make sense of conflicting data sources.
- And much more.

To state the obvious, blockchain will eliminate millions of jobs. Technology always does in its inexorable march forward. People who refuse to adapt and learn new skills will struggle to find new jobs.

Finally, much like generative AI, expect more software applications to adopt blockchain as an essential feature.

Blockchain Tech Will Soon Become Ubiquitous and Essential

The topic of Chapter 5, generative AI, may have amazed you. For two reasons, it also should have terrified you. First, a deepfake can already wreak havoc. Case in point: in May 2022, pro-Russian propagandists created a video of Ukrainian President Volodymyr Zelenskyy allegedly telling his country's troops to surrender.[29] The video wasn't real, but the quality of deepfakes will only improve.

Second, spam is annoying but generally obvious *now*. Generative AI will soon take social engineering to a new level. Hacks will become more sophisticated and effective. Get ready for much more plausible ones.

At least experts are aware of the problem and working to solve it. For example, Adobe is developing a feature called *Content Credentials*. It allows "creators to add their attribution details to their exported images."[30] The company is also collaborating with Microsoft on a deepfake polygraph.[31]

Count the *Wall Street Journal*, BBC, the *New York Times*, and Twitter among the more than nine hundred companies that have agreed to display a simple yet powerful Content Credentials button. With a single click, viewers can easily view the provenance and entire lifecycle of a video, photo, or other piece of content.

Combatting bad actors won't be easy, but this much is certain: blockchain and smart-contract technologies represent some of our best tools to prevent society from devolving into utter chaos.[32]

Key Points

- The parties involved in a blockchain-based transaction can't muck with the data on it.
- Healthcare, banking, supply chain, and real estate are just a few of the industries poised to benefit from blockchain. Its potential to transform business processes and even entire sectors is hard to overstate.
- Blockchain investors realize its vast potential and have been chomping at the bit.
- The widespread adoption of blockchain technology will profoundly affect the workplace and millions of workers.

CHAPTER 7
Immersive Technologies

What happens when doing your job blurs with playing a video game? We're about to find out.

"Soccer is America's sport of the future—and always will be."

—KEITH OLBERMANN

For twenty-five years, Kay Bartulis had lived with *spinal stenosis*: the space inside her backbone was too small. The condition caused her a great deal of pain and impeded her everyday life. As she told the local CBS affiliate, "I couldn't walk far. I'd have to stop, take a break, walk a bit, stop, and take a break."[1]

On June 8, 2020, she went under the knife. Johns Hopkins Hospital surgeons performed the first two procedures. In the first, the doctors:

placed six screws in a patient's spine for spinal fusion surgery to fuse three vertebrae in order to relieve the patient's chronic, debilitating back pain. For the second surgery on June 10, surgeons removed a cancerous tumor known as a chordoma from the spine of a patient.[2]

I'll cut to the chase: the surgery went swimmingly well. Bartulis now feels great. She calls it a miracle.

It's a great story but, at first glance, a relatively unexceptional one. Back surgeries aren't exactly uncommon these days. The number exploded nearly eightfold between 1993 and 2011, reaching 465,000.[3] (It now stands at about 500,000.[4]) But there was something special about Bartulis's operations—specifically, the tools and technology that her surgeons used.

Previous procedures of this type required surgeons to frequently shift their gazes back and forth between their screens and their patients. Most still do. When neurosurgeon Dr. Tim Witham operated on Bartulis, though, he wore a sophisticated headset that gave him the best of both worlds. The apparatus allowed Witham to concurrently view a full CT scan that overlaid Bartulis's body. As a result, he knew where to place the screws in her spine with an unprecedented level of precision.

In a subsequent video, Witham described the operation as the first "augmented-reality-guided procedure for placement of spinal instrumentation."* In his words:

> We take a computer image and place that image on the view of the real world. This allows for tremendous accuracy and precision. It's added confidence for the surgeon

---

* Watch the video at https://tinyurl.com/ps-ar-spine.

that we are placing the instrumentation correctly and accurately.

Let me repeat: surgeons can now bring cutting-edge, critical, and minimally invasive technology *inside patients' bodies.*

Bartulis was the first beneficiary of augmented reality in the operating room but certainly not the last. Since that time, Witham reports having successfully performed dozens of similar surgeries. Other hospitals have also adopted the technology, including UConn Health.[5]

And there's nothing all that special about backs and the use of AR. In the future, medical uses of immersive technologies will become commonplace. What's more, they're coming to every workplace.

Background and Definitions

Much like blockchain, there's no single, universally accepted definition of *immersive technologies.* They run the gamut. To keep things as simple as possible and avoid jargon, think of them as technologies that fuse the physical world with the digital one.

Immersive tech is an umbrella term that covers several related fields and adjacent concepts. Table 7.1 provides brief synopses of them.

Term	Brief Definition
Virtual reality	Britannica defines it as "the use of computer modeling and simulation that enables a person to interact with an artificial three-dimensional (3-D) visual or other sensory environment."[6]
Augmented reality	Here I'll borrow from Gartner: "The real-time use of information in the form of text, graphics, audio, and other virtual enhancements integrated with real-world objects."[7]

Term	Brief Definition
Mixed reality	When you put real and virtual objects in the microwave and press Cook for ten minutes, you wind up with MR. That's my colorful take on the 1994 original definition from academics Paul Milgram and Fumio Kishino.[8]
Extended reality	Extended reality (XR) covers VR, AR, MR, and other future realities. (You know, because we don't have enough of them already.) Also, it includes haptics and holograms.
Spatial computing	Simon Greenwold originally described it as "the interaction with a machine in which the machine retains and manipulates referents to real objects and spaces."[9] In other words, it understands its digital twin.
Digital twin	This is a virtual model of a physical object.
Metaverse	The author Neal Stephenson described it as follows in his 1992 sci-fi book *Snow Crash*: "A shared virtual space where people can interact with each other and with virtual objects and environments."

Table 7.1: Defining Immersive Technologies

For our purposes, the term *immersive technologies* is sufficient. Readers won't benefit from a pronounced comparison of the elements in Table 7.1.

Recent VR Forays

Keith Olbermann's quote at the beginning of the chapter about soccer could just as easily apply here: virtual reality is the future, and it always will be. Over the past ten years alone, some of the largest tech companies in the world have tried mashing together bits and atoms.

A few weeks after Facebook acquired Oculus for about $2 billion, Google Glass debuted in April 2013. (I soon gave the latter a test drive at a Las Vegas networking event.* Yes, I was a glasshole

---

* Read my post about the experience at https://tinyurl.com/ps-googl-gl.

for a hot minute.) Despite Google's lofty aspirations for its smart glasses, it remained a niche product. That reality—pun intended— hasn't stopped others from trying to crack the VR nut.

Microsoft launched HoloLens on March 30, 2016. The company's layoffs in January 2023 "effectively kill[ed] HoloLens and its mixed-reality projects."[10] In fairness, Microsoft Mesh seems alive and well. Snap's Spectacles arrived seven months later. CEO Evan Spiegel has said that it may take another decade for the glasses to enter the mainstream.[11] In collaboration with Ray-Ban, Meta launched a pair of smart glasses in September 2021. Sales results have been underwhelming so far.[12]

Are all consumer headsets and wearable face tech tchotchkes destined to find niche audiences at best?

We'll soon find out.

Apple Is Coming

After years of delays, Apple is finally poised to debut its long-awaited XR headset in 2023.[13] For immersive technologies, will the device—costing a reported $3,000—be the canary in the coal mine?

Nobody knows, but the company has pulled off similar coups before. After all, Apple didn't create the first MP3 player with its 2001 iPod. That honor belongs to SaeHan Information Systems and its 1997 product, the MPMan F10. Apple also didn't invent the cellphone; it *reinvented* the category on June 29, 2007, when it announced the iPhone.

In a way, whether consumers embrace Apple's latest shiny new thing is moot. Immersive tech has already permeated the workplace.

Immersive Tech in Action

Applephiles and hardcore gamers may be waiting for the company's forthcoming product, but some companies have already hopped on the VR/AR train.

Walmart Embraces High-Tech Employee Training

In 2017, Walmart began using Oculus Rift VR headsets in its training centers, dubbed Walmart Academies. Thanks to VR, the company has gained new insights into employee skills. It has used the technology to deliver training to employees in innovative ways. What's more, the results have been encouraging. Walmart has seen improvements in employee test scores from VR-based training sessions.

In the words of Andy Trainor, the company's vice president of learning:

> When we used the Oculus Rift VR headset in the classroom, we noticed an increase in test scores between 5 percent and 10 percent. We are starting to replace some global learning management system modules that can take 30 to 45 minutes and transitioning this to a three- to five-minute module in the virtual reality environment.
>
> Obviously, you don't have the opportunity to train after hours, and you don't want to disrupt your customers on the floor. Virtual reality allows you to artificially create safe scenarios that you can't re-create on the sales floor.[14]

Walmart executives have found that VR works especially well when rolling out new technology and processes. UPS and Fidelity have also successfully incorporated VR into existing training programs.

Accenture Reimagines Meetings, Collaboration, and Onboarding

Accenture is an IT consulting outfit employing more than 700,000 people. Its advisory services include network security, cloud computing, and change management. Why not make a few bucks helping others make sense of the mysterious metaverse?[15]

But how can Accenture advisors justify their steep rates here if their company hasn't walked the talk?

I'd be gobsmacked if Accenture bigwigs weren't asking themselves that question in the weeks preceding March 2022. In the middle of that month, the company published a new page on its website promoting its metaverse offerings. (Thank you, Internet Archive.)

At the same time (give or take), the company detailed its internal efforts to fuse the physical and digital worlds:

> Accenture's enterprise metaverse, known as the Nth floor, refers to the virtual environments we have created to bring Accenture people together to meet, collaborate, and learn. Whether hosting meetings or socializing, the metaverse is a versatile, scalable solution for bringing a geographically distributed workforce together.
>
> In addition, Accenture has created digital twins of many of its physical offices, from Bangalore in India to Madrid in Spain and San Francisco in the United States, to provide familiar environments for its people to meet, collaborate, and network.[16]

Accenture is eating its own dog food, in the parlance of Silicon Valley. The company reported that 150,000 new hires worked from its metaverse on their first day. Thousands more have attended company events and training sessions in it.*

To help usher in this era and promote the company's offerings, some Accenture employees are wisely incorporating the Nth floor into their social media presences. Figure 7.1 displays the LinkedIn profile of Jason Warnke, its digital experiences lead.

Figure 7.1: LinkedIn Profile of Jason Warnke, Source: LinkedIn, Accenture

Expect more organizations to follow the leads of Accenture and Walmart, especially regarding employee training.

The Floodgates Will Open

Jeremy Bailenson is a professor of communication at Stanford University and the founding director of the Virtual Human Interaction Lab. As he writes in his 2018 book *Experience on Demand*:

---

* Watch a quick video of it at https://tinyurl.com/ps9-accenture.

For me the most exciting aspect of VR instruction is its potential to democratize learning and training. To be sure, it won't be as easy as uploading a kung fu program in a few seconds, like Neo does in *The Matrix*. Learning expert skills takes dedication and focus and lots and lots of practice. But it does mean that eventually everyone will have access to resources that, should they be willing to put in the work, can put them on the path to expert performance.

In interviews, Bailenson has gushed about the rapid progress that immersive technologies have made in the past few years. With respect to training, he sees strong parallels between online courses and VR.

It's no biggie that we can take college courses online or buy them piecemeal on MasterClass, Teachable, Thinkific, and other marketplaces. In the not too distant future, we'll say the same about immersive technologies, such as VR and AR, especially as tech companies improve their devices and add new features.

Building a Better Mousetrap

But your organization probably isn't in a position like Accenture. It can't drop hundreds of thousands of dollars to create a bespoke metaverse. You may think that the benefits of immersive technologies will elude you.

Think again.

Zoom

Over the past eighteen months, few companies' stock prices have fallen as precipitously as Zoom's. We're talking about a freefall of greater than 80 percent. Against that backdrop, the company hasn't been in a position to make pricey acquisitions or devote billions to building the metaverse, as Mark Zuckerberg has with Meta.

In September 2021, Zoom did the next best thing and announced a partnership with Meta. Users can now experience VR on their Zoom calls, as long as they're using Meta's Horizon Workrooms on supported Oculus equipment.[17]

If that sounds like a mouthful (and it certainly is), there are simpler, lower tech ways to get a less immersive experience in native Zoom. In late 2022, the company released a feature that lets users create custom human avatars for meetings.[18] Figure 7.2 shows my Zoom avatar.

Figure 7.2: My Zoom Avatar, Source: Zoom, Phil Simon

No, this simple feature won't win any design awards. Still, if I haven't put my face on yet, I'd rather show attendees a PG, virtual version of myself than a silly cat avatar or nothing during an early Zoom call.

Microsoft

You'd be correct in thinking that all this hardware and software feels a bit disjointed. Those yearning for a simple, all-encompassing solution may be in luck. Microsoft Mesh is the company's ambitious new attempt at fusing:

- Holograms.
- Different kinds of wearable devices, including its Holo-Lens and other VR and AR headsets.
- Laptops.
- Smartphones.
- Collaboration software, specifically Microsoft Teams.

Its tagline is, "Here can be anywhere."

Mesh just doesn't purport to be an app or even a metaverse. Microsoft is also branding it as a *platform* for which third-party developers will want to build cool apps.*

Figure 7.3 on the next page shows a screenshot of what the company has already built.

Workplace Considerations

Compared to their counterparts in the physical world, activities that take place through AR, VR, MR, or other immersive technologies lend themselves to automatic, real-time data collection. At this point, it's natural to ask a simple question: is this a good or a bad thing?

The answer is *yes*.

---

* This marketing approach is a bit muddled. Are you an app, a metaphor, or a platform? All of the above. *Sheesh.*

Figure 7.3: Microsoft Mesh Screenshot, Source: Microsoft

The Double-Edged Sword of Gamification

"The Strike" is the tenth episode of the final season of *Seinfeld*. In it, Elaine dutifully eats flavorless sandwiches because, when she reaches twenty-four, Atomic Subs will give her a free one.* As she scolds a disapproving Jerry at Monk's Café, "Hey! I have spent a lot of time, and I have eaten a lot of crap to get to where I am today. And I am not throwing it all away now."

The episode first aired on December 18, 1997. As usual, the show was years ahead of its time.

Merriam-Webster defines gamification as "the process of adding games or gamelike elements to something (such as a task) so as to encourage participation."[19] The concept is rooted in behavioral economics. Beyond force-feeding yourself mediocre subs, *encouraging participation* encompasses an extensive array of behaviors. Loads of studies have confirmed its general ability to:

- Engage and motivate individuals.[20]
- Provide accountability and transparency.

---

* See https://tinyurl.com/ps-the-9-sub.

- Produce better results for individuals, teams, and organizations.

Sweden famously gamified safe driving.[21] In the private sector, scores of companies have used the technique to make their products *stickier*. As but one example, consider the dating app Tinder. Its "gamelike user experience enticed overlooked users, led to rapid segment growth, and ultimately displaced industry incumbents."[22]

Take *that*, eHarmony!

For better or worse, Tinder turned online dating into a game. It worked because we humans are competitive; we like to win games. Paradoxically, we don't want to know *when* we'll win. People wouldn't play slot machines if their payouts were even and predictable. Whether we realize it or not, we also like to win *randomly*.

Natasha Schüll is an anthropologist and expert on slot machines. In her 2012 book *Addiction by Design: Machine Gambling in Las Vegas*, she describes how players sitting at *Megabucks* or *Wheel of Fortune* mentally check out. They unknowingly enter what she calls a *ludic loop*. (In Latin, *ludus* means "game, play, sport, pastime, entertainment, or fun.") If you've ever played *Tetris*, you know the feeling.

Sometimes, to begin or finish a game, we need a kick in the ass. Uber understands the concept of *nudges* all too well—and has since its inception.

In his 2017 piece in the *New York Times*, Noam Scheiber peeled back the curtain on the ride-sharing behemoth's extensive use of behavioral economics and gamification. It's worth quoting at some length:

Uber, for its part, appears to be aware of the ludic loop. In its messages to drivers, it included a graphic of an engine gauge with a needle that came tantalizingly close to, but was still short of, a dollar sign.

And the ludic loop is far from the only video game feature that Uber has adopted as a way of keeping drivers on the road.

At any moment, the app shows drivers how many trips they have taken in the current week, how much money they have made, how much time they have spent logged on and what their overall rating from passengers is. All of these metrics can stimulate the competitive juices that drive compulsive game-playing.

"The whole thing is like a video game," said Eli Solomon, a veteran Uber and Lyft driver in the Chicago area, who said he sometimes had to fight the urge to work more after glancing at his data.[23]

Why use the app to nudge drivers to keep driving? Why not just order them to go to work?

Money, of course.

Recall from Chapter 2 that bosses are insisting that all employees return to the office. This demand wouldn't fly at Uber, and not because its drivers make money by driving. The company can't compel its drivers to go to work. Legally speaking, Uber drivers are independent contractors, not employees. As such, state labor laws around minimum wage, overtime, and workers' compensation don't apply to them, and Uber is determined to keep it that way.

In 2020, Lyft, DoorDash, Uber, and other gig-economy companies spent $224 million to pass Proposition 22 in California.[24] They succeeded—sort of. The measure passed, although a California judge invalidated it on constitutional grounds in August 2021.[25] Stay tuned.

Gamification gets us to do things that we wouldn't normally do, and do them for longer periods of time. But that's far from its sole side effect.

David Rose broaches additional concerns on the subject in *SuperSight*, his book about AR. As he writes:

> Others feel oppressed when managers track performance in detail. For them, accountability triggers feelings of anxiety and fear. There's also a legitimate concern that gamification may trivialize serious issues, reinforce a cutthroat mindset, and contaminate authentic passion and intrinsic motivation.

The immersive technologies discussed in this chapter lend themselves to gamification. (After all, millions of people use them to play video games.) As we'll see in the next chapter, the propensity to quantify everything is a natural management instinct—and often a counterproductive one.

Addressing Zoom Fatigue

As the pandemic wore on, we experienced Zoom fatigue. Stanford researchers, including our friend Jeremy Bailenson, ultimately homed in on its four causes:

1. We find excessive periods of close-up eye contact jarring.
2. Seeing ourselves during video chats quickly tires us out.
3. Video calls dramatically reduce our natural mobility.

4. They also increase our *cognitive load*. We have to process and remember more inputs.[26]

Let's not demonize Zoom, the tool that became the *de facto* standard for online meetings during lockdown. Had the pandemic occurred in 2010, we would have called the same condition *Skype fatigue*. At one point, Skype had amassed more than 650 million users.[27] (Talk about dropping the ball, but I digress.)

To minimize Zoom fatigue, we can easily disable our webcams or turn off Self View. Fine, but those are just Band-Aids. AR, VR, and other immersive technologies will never truly compete with— never mind replace—real-world workplaces until they solve the four problems mentioned earlier.

At least we're aware of the issues and are working to develop solutions. Microsoft, for one, has conducted extensive research on the matter. In July 2020, the company launched Together Mode for Microsoft Teams. Think of it as a way of placing all meeting participants in the same virtual auditorium, coffee shop, or conference room.[28]

As it turns out, finding a common location—even a virtual one—really matters. It increases what Canadian cognitive scientist Abigail Sellen calls *reciprocity*. As she explains:

> When we're in a room together, we have reciprocity. If I can see you, you can see me. If I can hear you, you can hear me, and we know how each other is perceived. As soon as we get mediated by technology, we have uncertainties. We lose our ability to perform in relation to one another, to engage with one another. Big-picture thinking as a team becomes really difficult in the situation we're in right now. [29]

Microsoft isn't alone. Startups and academic projects are also tackling the challenges plaguing virtual meetings and remote work. For instance, the mmhmm app from All Turtles allows users to level the playing field and, for good measure, add a little panache to our virtual meetings and presentations.

Chapter 2 revealed that remote and hybrid work are here to stay. Along these lines, expect a great deal more innovation around immersive technologies in the years to come. If you're dubious, recall the key improvements that Zoom made over Skype, Webex, and other first-generation videoconferencing tools. Breakout rooms, reduced latency, and the ability to reach much larger audiences come to mind. Zoom proved that Skype and Webex didn't represent the best we could do. The incumbents' product managers and senior leadership became complacent, opening the door for a nimble competitor built on better tech.

Other Issues

We've been talking about fusing the real and virtual worlds for decades. The journey hasn't been easy. Additional issues include:

- **Bandwidth, equity, and access:** VR, AR, and MR applications aren't exactly lightweight. More than ten million citizens in the US currently lack access to high-speed internet connectivity.[30] How do we make the playing field as even as possible for them?
- **Drawing lines:** In theory, it's easy—or at least *easier*—for us to leave our jobs at the office when we leave the office. How will we react when new devices and software can interrupt us no matter where we are and what we're doing?

- **Long-term health:** How will these new immersive technologies affect our mental health? Will we burn out quicker? Will VR devices cause motion sickness and other maladies?
- **Norms and laws:** Workplace laws prohibit sexual harassment, gender-based discrimination, and other types of behavior. Will those laws apply in the metaverse or whatever you want to call it? We just don't know.[31]

There are still tons of logistical and technological problems to solve, but the adoption of immersive technologies will only intensify. The era of near-universal in-office work is over; the opportunity is just too vast.

Key Points

- The umbrella term *immersive technologies* encompasses VR, AR, MR, and the metaverse.
- Walmart and Accenture are just two of the companies that have already benefited from their use.
- Immersive technologies can do much more than reduce Zoom fatigue.
- Gamification is a double-edged sword. It can promote both constructive and destructive behaviors.

CHAPTER 8
Unhealthy Analytics

The spotlight is about to shine brightly on a whole new class of employees.

"If you torture the data enough, nature will always confess."
—RONALD COASE

Even on its best day, baseball has never been the most exciting sport. Homer Simpson once famously quipped, "I never realized how boring this game is without beer."* In terms of action, no one would ever mistake it for professional football.

Baseball's true fans, however, would never use the b-word. They've long appreciated the game's subtlety and strategy, not to

---

* "Duffless" is the sixteenth episode of Season 4 of the show and one of my faves.

mention the insane skill required to make contact with a spinning object moving so damn fast. A unique blend of physics and neuroscience makes hitting a baseball "astronomically difficult." In fact, it's the hardest skill in sports to master.[1] The *best* hitters fail seven times out of ten.

It's called *America's pastime* for a reason. Baseball history is nothing if not storied. The first known game in the United States took place on October 6, 1845. The New York Nine obliterated the Knickerbockers 23-1 in four innings at Elysian Fields in Hoboken, New Jersey.[2]

For nearly two hundred years, the game has evolved in more ways than I can count. In the early twentieth century, players commonly worked part-time jobs in the offseason because of their paltry salaries. (Seriously.) The steroid era of the 1990s produced synthetic man mountains who shattered hallowed home run records. The most significant change to the game in my lifetime and perhaps ever, though, has involved the use of—and purists would say *misuse* of—analytics.

Advanced Analytics Break Baseball

Whether you're a diehard or know nothing about the sport, you've probably heard of *Moneyball*. Michael Lewis's bestselling 2004 book details the story of Billy Beane, then the general manager of the Oakland Athletics. Unable to compete with the Yankees, the Red Sox, and other big-market clubs for free agents, Beane had to get creative. He struck gold in Sabermetrics, statistician Bill James's long-ignored work on how to really evaluate baseball players.

The results were phenomenal. Despite severe financial constraints, the A's weren't just competitive; the team consistently punched well above its weight. Starting in 2002, it made the League Divisional Series for four consecutive years by eschewing baseball orthodoxy. Between August 13 and September 4, 2002, Beane's ragtag bunch of bargain-bin players won an astonishing twenty straight games.

It was a great story, and Hollywood agreed. In 2011, *Moneyball* starring Brad Pitt ultimately hit the big screen.

So, what's the problem?

In a word, *analytics*.

For the A's, the cat was out of the bag. Even deep-pocketed teams started adopting Beane's methods. (The Boston Red Sox even offered him their GM job. He declined.) The powerful force of analytics soon changed the game in profound ways.

Games started lasting longer. In 1978, the average one took two-and-a-half hours to complete. By 2021, that number had ballooned 28 percent to three hours and eleven minutes.[3] Not great in an era of TikTok videos and short attention spans.

Even worse, games were generally dull and even unwatchable. Yes, home runs increased, but so did strikeouts and pitching changes. Stolen bases and batting averages declined.[4] New technology gave birth to advanced metrics. For example, hitters could now track their launch angles, defined as "the vertical angle at which the ball leaves a player's bat after being struck."[5] They became obsessed. More home runs meant more lucrative contracts, strikeouts be damned.

Fewer balls in play resulted in less action for players and fans alike. When batters *did* put the ball in play, would-be singles and doubles from years past became routine groundouts. Managers routinely shifted shortstops, second basemen, and outfielders to unnatural positions on the field. They also constantly swapped out relief pitchers. In each case, that's what the data told them to do.

Baseball didn't used to be this way.

Over his twenty-three-year hall-of-fame career ending in 2008, Greg Maddux was a pitching maestro. He won 355 games, but not by bringing the gas. When he got a batter down 0-2, he tried "to throw a strike to induce weak contact. If he struck the batter out, all the better."[6]

The general public's interest in analytics-driven baseball was waning—something that the data not so ironically reflected. Exhibit A: in 2022, the Houston Astros won the World Series by ousting the Philadelphia Phillies 4-2. On average, a mere 11.8 million viewers watched each game, the second-lowest TV ratings ever.[7] (To be fair, other sporting events experienced similar declines during the pandemic.[8])

Exhibit B: the decline in tickets sold. Ignore the 2020 season with no fans in attendance. And sure, in 2021, nearly all ballparks started with capacity restrictions, so there were fewer butts in the seats. But even the return to normal in 2022 marked the lowest attended season since 1997.[9]

At least Major League Baseball has recognized the problem, although some have argued that it moved far too slowly. Starting in 2023, the league instituted a pitch timer, limits on defensive shifts, three-batter minimums for relief pitchers, and slightly larger bases. (MLB experimented in the minor leagues and found that the latter resulted in significantly increased per-game steal attempts and success rates.[10])

Ideally, the changes will make games shorter and more exciting.

At first, the use of analytics was benign and, in the case of the Oakland A's, necessary. Quantifying everything, though, drastically changed baseball—and even temporarily broke it. In this chapter, we'll see how it will do the same with the workforce.

Before I do, though, a disclaimer is in order.

The Downsides of Data-Driven Decision-Making

In this chapter, I dunk on the overuse and misuse of data in several areas. Readers unfamiliar with my previous work may understandably believe I'm a dataphobe.

Nothing could be further from the truth.

Three of my books espouse the virtues of intelligently using data. Companies like Google, Netflix, and Amazon have gleaned fascinating insights from their troves of data, and much of their success stems from it. I also used to teach a capstone course on analytics to college seniors.

The idea, though, that data, analytics, and algorithms *always* result in a superior, defensible, and equitable outcome is preposterous. (See the Coase quote at the start of this chapter. Better yet, give Cathy O'Neil's bestseller *Weapons of Math Destruction* a read.) All too often, data provides merely the veneer of objectivity, facts, and truth.

Using data to make any decision guarantees precisely nothing. The list of firms that made regrettable decisions despite using it is long and distinguished. Chapter 6 detailed one of them: JPMorgan Chase. No doubt Frank's four million users factored heavily into the bank's decision to pony up $175 million for the startup.

The Roots of Contemporary Analytics

Count Jeff Bezos, Jack Welch, and Steve Jobs among the most influential chief executives of the modern business landscape. To be sure, each leader was controversial in his own way. (Jobs's reality distortion field is the stuff of legend.) For decades, an ethically challenged management theorist who died more than a century ago has arguably exerted more influence than the troika combined.

It's time to meet Frederick Winslow Taylor.

In the late nineteenth century, Taylor studied factory workers as they performed different manual tasks. He meticulously recorded everything he saw with his stopwatch. He was convinced there was a single, optimal way to complete each task, and he was determined to discover it. In 1881, while working at a plant in Midvale, Pennsylvania, he introduced his theory of time and motion study.

Enduring Impact Despite Questionable Methods

Taylor frequently and loudly touted the results of one of his experiments. It involved how much pig iron workers should be able to move each day: forty-seven tons, in case you were curious.*

Sounds all scientific, eh? Unfortunately, Taylor liked to play loose with the facts. As Matthew Stewart wrote in his 2009 book *The Management Myth*:

> Frederick Winslow Taylor told the pig-iron story so often and so well that for more than half a century after his death, critics and sympathizers alike simply assumed it was true. But it was not.

---

* Read about it if you like at https://tinyurl.com/ps-pig-iron.

Nevertheless, Taylor's star continued to rise, and he was quick to cash in. He shopped his talents to prominent managers of the day eager to find a true efficiency expert, most notably at Bethlehem Steel. The University of Pennsylvania awarded him an honorary degree in 1906.[11] That same year, he became president of the American Society of Mechanical Engineers.[12] Taylor codified his work in his 1911 monograph, *The Principles of Scientific Management.*

Taylor's exaggerations, outright fabrications (yes, plural), and even his death in 1915 didn't curb the business community's enthusiasm for his work. He had hit a nerve—one that transcended the business press. I can't decide which of the following facts is more fascinating:

- Aldous Huxley skewered Taylorism in his dystopian 1932 book *Brave New World.*
- Charlie Chaplin also crucified Taylorism in his black comedy *Modern Times* a few years later.

Beyond classic texts and movies, Taylor's posthumous impact was particularly acute across institutions of higher education. To quote from the book *The Management Myth* again:

> In 1959 for example, the highly influential Gordon and Howell report on the state of business education called for a reinvigoration of the scientific foundations of business education.

Beginning in the 1970s, Taylorism started falling out of favor in mainstream management circles. Gurus, progressive business leaders, and labor unions rejected the notion that one can and should precisely measure and prescribe all employee actions and output. Doing so dehumanizes work.

Of course, some have held out. That is, reports of Taylorism's demise were greatly exaggerated. It's making a bit of a comeback, and one could argue that it never really disappeared.

The Constant Pressure to Make Rate

Amazon places enormous pressure on all its employees. Its pickers need to *make rate*—that is, to "keep up with the hourly stow, pick, or scan rates expected of them."[13] Employees at its massive distribution centers are effectively work-athletes who, just like NFL and NBA players, frequently use their days off to recover from the physical poundings that their bodies have taken.* Former job posts required workers to stand on their feet for around nine hours and walk 10–15 miles daily.[14]

The picker job is so grueling and suffers from so much turnover that Amazon's top brass worries that the company will soon run out of people to hire, according to a leaked June 2022 internal memo.[15] Some have labeled Amazon's practices *neo-Taylorism* or *Digital Taylorism*.[16] They're not wrong.

At least pickers aren't alone. Amazon delivery drivers also face ambitious—and some would argue, unreasonable—routes, thresholds, and timelines. Reports of male drivers peeing in water bottles to save precious time persist.[17]

As mentioned in Chapter 4, Amazon long ago rolled out sophisticated robots. For now, though, they can only do so much. For the time being, The Everything Store needs human beings to keep the machine operating. It will be fascinating to see whether and how the company adapts its stringent metrics in the face of a

---

* Check out the PBS Frontline documentary *Amazon Empire: The Rise and Reign of Jeff Bezos*.

dwindling supply of workers and the likelihood of unionization at several of its locations. Stay tuned.

Outside of Amazon, plenty of workers don't think twice about their employers' routine monitoring and exacting standards. Manufacturing environments wouldn't be nearly as efficient had they not employed Total Quality Management and Six Sigma decades ago. Beyond factories, call center reps need to hit hourly call quotas. Thanks to technology, it's easy to accurately measure specific tasks, such as the number of deliveries an Amazon driver makes or an Uber driver's average rating.

But is the same true with more complex knowledge work? What about the behaviors and actions that white-collar workers need to exhibit? How 'bout them apples?

It's time to talk about traditional performance management.

The State of Employee Performance Management

Let me be blunt: employees mostly loathe performance reviews. I'd be shocked if you felt otherwise. Consider the results of a 2017 Gallup poll:

> A mere 14 percent of employees strongly agree that the performance reviews they receive inspire them to improve, and only 2 in 10 employees strongly agree that their performance is managed in a way that motivates them to do outstanding work.[18]

I've seen this movie before. During my brief stint in HR at CapitalOne out of grad school, I observed firsthand the process of evaluating managers and directors. HR-led group calibration sessions soon devolved into contentious discussions over which employees should receive which rating.

You might equate your performance review with your semi-annual trip to the dentist. No one *likes* getting their teeth scraped, but the benefits of regular cleanings far exceed their costs. Does the same principle apply when you sit down with your boss to review your performance over the past year?

In general, no. With rare exceptions, annual performance reviews are, well, performative. They've *never* really and consistently accomplished their stated goals: motivating employees and changing their behavior. So says Robert Sutton, a professor of management science and engineering at Stanford University:

> In most organizations, traditional performance reviews are so bad they do more harm than good. The way human beings make progress is through small steps, not through a bizarre conversation once a year.[19]

A trove of academic research questions—if not outright impugns—the efficacy of annual reviews. Rare is the journal article that has historically found them effective.

Let's explore a few lesser-known reasons that our considerable efforts to accurately measure employee performance have borne so little fruit.

Goodhart's Law

We can't very well evaluate employees without telling them in advance precisely how we're going to do that.

And therein lies the problem.

At this point, I'll cede the floor to the British economist Charles Goodhart. Speaking at a conference in Sydney, Australia, in 1975, he said, "Any observed statistical regularity will tend to collapse once pressure is placed upon it for control purposes."

Two decades later, the British anthropologist Marilyn Strathern refined Goodhart's wise but clunky statement into what we now know as *Goodhart's Law*: "When a measure becomes a target, it ceases to be a good measure."[20] Figure 8.1 makes the concept even more digestible.

Figure 8.1: Goodhart's Law

Goodhart's Law is universal. We face strong, often irresistible incentives to modify our behavior and improve our outcomes. Examples are just about everywhere:

> In higher education, colleges manipulated their data to achieve a higher spot in the influential *US News & World Report* rankings. Since the number of applications counts, some colleges counted every postcard expressing interest as an application. And since a high rejection rate is

considered prestigious, some colleges "rejected" applicants for fall admission, only to admit them for the spring
semester.[21]

Staying in this lane for a moment, let's return to our friend Dr.
Maitland Jones from Chapter 1. You'll recall the NYU professor
who lost his job for refusing to cave into student demands. Although probably the most public case in recent memory, Dr. Jones
is hardly the only prof whose students wanted him to chillax. The
org chem professor held firm, but will others do the same when
students bitch and moan?

Based on my experience, I'm dubious.

Department chairs routinely look at student class evaluations
when deciding to extend offers to contingent faculty for the next
academic year. (In fairness, it's neither the sole nor the most important factor in these decisions.) As such, lecturers and instruc-
tors have occasionally made their exams and assignments easier
to improve their evaluations. Of course, the students are the ones
who ultimately suffer.

Campbell's Law

Think of Goodhart's Law as the second cousin of Campbell's
Law. As the psychologist and social scientist Donald T. Campbell
wrote in a 1979 journal article:

> The more any quantitative social indicator is used for so-
> cial decision-making, the more subject it will be to cor-
> ruption pressures and the more apt it will be to distort and
> corrupt the social processes it is intended to monitor.[22]

Let's tighten that up a skosh: when you define success in terms of a specific measure, you reduce its ability to accurately measure that success. And yes, this applies to all types of workers—even software developers.

How Not to Evaluate Coders

In November 2022, Elon Musk unceremoniously shitcanned half of Twitter's 7,500 employees. Chaos ensued among current and former employees, users, and advertisers.[23] Rumors swirled about who lost their jobs and why.

One rumor made the rounds, occasionally on Twitter itself: software engineers who didn't contribute enough lines of code to the company's codebase got their walking papers. (Thanks to metadata and modern source-code-management tools like Bitbucket and GitLens, determining exactly which coders did what and when is straightforward and takes seconds.)

Let me be crystal clear: although I disagree with Musk's approach to the dismissals, I don't know if he axed programmers based on this crude measure. I'm not implying otherwise. Anecdotally over the years, it would be naïve to suggest that it's never happened when managers needed to scalp a few heads.

Firing coders solely by looking at lines of code generated or committed is bush league, but don't take my word for it. Bill Gates once said, "Measuring programming progress by lines of code is like measuring aircraft building progress by weight."

A friend of mine is an über-talented full-stack developer at a large tech company. Some of his unscrupulous peers intentionally introduced minor bugs so they could fix them later. They wrote empty functions and defined them the next

day. Both stratagems allowed them to score more points with
their managers who lacked programming backgrounds.

The reason is simple and harkens back to Goodhart's Law.
Marginal programmers wrote and committed inefficient code
to satisfy arbitrary corporate thresholds. They submitted fixes
or improvements later, ostensibly proving their value.

The Hawthorne Effect

Western Electric had a good run as an outfit—better than most,
in fact. Originally founded in 1869, the electrical engineering and
manufacturing company lasted until 1984. Nearly four decades after the company closed its doors, its legacy lives on.

Between 1924 and 1932, researchers at the Hawthorne Works,
one of its large factory complexes in Cicero, Illinois, conducted a
series of studies called the Illumination Experiments. The group
was interested in the relationship between workplace lighting and
worker productivity. Did one affect the other? How? As it turned
out, almost *any* change in the former yielded increases in the latter.

In the 1950s, sociologist Henry Landsberger analyzed those
studies and ultimately published the results of his findings.[24] Yes,
workers in the Hawthorne Works study were more productive, but
that facile statement didn't tell the whole story. Not even close.

Landsberger found that the productivity bump didn't stem
from the amount of light in the factory. (More on that in a minute.)
Instead, it emanated from the fact that the workers knew they were
part of an experiment; they were special. As a result, they changed
their behavior and worked harder than they otherwise would have.

We have long referred to this phenomenon as the *Hawthorne effect*. Since Landsberger's findings, proper researchers have taken steps to prevent or minimize it. That is, they intentionally keep their studies' participants in the dark. (Ethically, this deception opens up Pandora's box. Cue Stanley Milgram reference.[25])

Research from 2011 has challenged Landsberger's conclusions. As Steven Levitt (of *Freakonomics* fame) and John List write in a paper for The National Bureau of Economic Research:

> We find that existing descriptions of supposedly remarkable data patterns prove to be entirely fictional. There are, however, hints of more subtle manifestations of a Hawthorne effect in the original data.[26]

Whether the Hawthorne effect actually exists in *proper experiments* and to what extent is debatable. In the workplace, however, it's hard to deny. Different managers and different financial incentives produce different—although typically rational—employee behaviors and outcomes. (That sentence sums up the first *Freakonomics* book pretty well, but I digress.) We all know managers who value face time and immediate responses to weekend messages. Ambitious employees tend to act accordingly (re: suck up).

A Light at the End of the Tunnel?

Perhaps I'm being too dismissive of managers' ability to measure employee output and performance in fair and accurate manners. After all, everyone is still trying to figure out this new world of work. As we saw in Chapter 2, experimentation isn't just useful; it's required. Be patient. We'll ultimately land on a method of accurately measuring employee productivity, won't we?

Fiverr is a popular marketplace that connects freelancers with individuals and companies needing their services. Its CEO and founder, Micha Kaufman, holds a sanguine view about the future of measuring employee productivity. Speaking to *The Economist* in January 2023, he opines that "firms are getting better at measuring workers' performance based on their actual output rather than time spent producing it."[27]

Kaufman may be spot-on. I can envision ways that technologies like blockchain can make individuals' actions and output more accurate and transparent. (See Chapter 6.) At the same time, another force in this book makes me more than a little skeptical.

The advances in generative AI discussed in Chapter 5 throw one hell of a wrench into the works. How will managers' balanced scorecards, dashboards, and objectives and key results (OKRs) account for tools that let employees rapidly churn out quality original content in a fraction of the time formerly required? And, knowing how managers evaluate them, how will workers respond, especially if management forces them to return to the office?

Talk about forces colliding.

Throwing in the Towel

HR heads of some prominent companies have taken a more pessimistic view. They've decided to stop rolling the boulder up the hill. That is, they've ditched formal annual reviews. Recent examples include Accenture, Adobe, Deloitte, Gap, KPMG, and Microsoft.

And those are just a few of the companies that have determined the outputs don't justify the inputs. I suspect that thousands of employees at each firm raised a glass upon hearing the news, but the celebration may not have lasted long.

Employers Put on the Green Eyeshades

Unlike most of their blue-collar counterparts, most knowledge workers have historically not had to deal with intrusive tech and constant monitoring.

Because of the pandemic, that has started to change.

Trust, Technology, and Tension

Trust issues between employees and their bosses are as old as capitalism itself. Historically, managers have felt far more comfortable observing and supervising their direct reports when everyone concurrently worked in the same physical office. For this reason, employers consistently resisted workers' pleas for flexibility and remote work, but don't believe me.

In May 2019, Harvard Business School and Boston Consulting Group released "Future Positive: How Companies Can Tap into Employee Optimism to Navigate Tomorrow's Workplace."[28] The sample sizes were impressive: 11,000 workers and 6,500 business leaders, respectively.

Not surprisingly, employees in the survey voiced their strong preferences for flexibility and remote work. Sadly, a mere 30 percent of organizations offered it. Can someone say *chasm*?

Why would such a large percentage of companies fail to offer their employees the option to occasionally work remotely in 2019? Plenty of respondents blamed the lack of sufficient technology. If the year was 1989, that answer might have held water. In 2019, it was bullshit. Powerful, affordable, user-friendly, and secure collaboration applications had existed for years. The issue was usually a matter of good, old-fashioned trust.

Then COVID-19 happened. Faced with no other choice, employers finally relented and acquiesced to their employees' wishes. Boom.

Fast-forward three years: managers largely feel that remote and hybrid work have gummed up the works. (Yeah, that trust thing again.) A Microsoft report released in September 2022 revealed that a mere one in eight business leaders expressed full confidence that their hybrid employees are productive while away from the office.[29] Scores of studies have proven otherwise, but this battle isn't about productivity; it's about control, pure and simple.

More and more, CEOs are demanding that employees return to the office. Case in point: on January 11, 2023, Starbucks CEO Howard Schultz told corporate employees to return to the office three days per week. Schultz knew the numbers. He cited "badging data [that] showed employees weren't adhering to a loose requirement to work from the office one to two days a week."[30]

Starbucks is no outlier. Scads of employers track when their employees come to the office and how long they're staying. (You'll recall from Chapter 2 Cisco's new office and its, er, impressive data collection capabilities.) As we'll see next, this type of monitoring isn't limited to physical locations.

The Rise of Employee Spyware

For years, employers have used powerful software to monitor what their employees are doing while on the clock, collect data, and alert managers of inactivity or concerning behavior. That's not to say that the practice was universal; it varied considerably. For obvious reasons, people working at government contractors and agencies were practically guaranteed to encounter enhanced security measures and strict computer protocols. Your tiny local law firm or four-employee family business? Not so much.

The post-COVID trends are unmistakable. First, senior managers and IT departments increasingly want to know what their employees are doing (and not doing) while on the clock, no matter where they are. Since March 2020, roughly one-third of medium-to-large US firms have adopted some kind of worker surveillance system.[31] One recent survey put the percentage of employers using this software on remote employees at 78.[32] It's hard to envision that number dropping anytime soon.

Second, companies are now especially interested in monitoring the activities of their white-collar workers. (As for why, see the previous section on trust.)

Jodi Kantor is a *New York Times* prize-winning investigative reporter and bestselling author. Appearing on *The Daily* podcast in August 2022, she describes how the pandemic both accelerated employee monitoring and expanded it to what was largely an unaffected group:

> It is moving up the income ladder into higher-paying jobs. But there was kind of a taint to it. A lot of companies hesitated to put this kind of tracking in place. And even some that did were embarrassed to talk about it. So this is quietly growing in the background. And then along comes the pandemic.
>
> All of a sudden, this kind of monitoring gets a new legitimacy because they're saying we can't see you. We don't know what our people are doing. We're no longer in day-to-day contact. We have to find a new way of working.

We are tools to get a better read on what is going on with our own workforce.

There was one boss I talked to who said, Jodi, I did not want to do this. I resisted it for a long time. But I had to implement this software because I had no idea where my people were. I would call them and they wouldn't call me back. And it was like a black hole. I did not want to do this. But this is what's necessary in the workplace now.[33]

Kantor astutely points out that knowledge workers typically haven't had to deal with monitoring software—certainly not to the same extent as offshore and domestic blue-collar workers have.

Against a rising tide of nosy bosses and state-of-the-art spyware, employees of all collars are getting creative. Amazon sells mouse jigglers to prevent computers from falling asleep and corporate software from detecting user inactivity on their computers.* In 2022, career coach Sho Dewan posted a 14-second TikTok video on how to keep his computer active by using basic PowerPoint functionality.[34] As of this writing, it has received a staggering 22 million views.

Hacks like these abound, and managers attempt to clamp down on employee attempts at deception. The cat-and-mouse game continues, feeding the never-ending cycle of mistrust depicted in Figure 8.2.

---

* Go nuts at https://tinyurl.com/ps-jiggler.

The Vicious Cycle of Employee Mistrust

Management
Distrusts
Employees

Increased
Surveillance &
Micromanagement

Increased Employee Resentment

Figure 8.2: The Vicious Cycle of Employee Mistrust

Of course, not everyone is trying to fool their employer. Plenty of employees don't realize that Big Brother is monitoring their keystrokes, browsing history, and logon times. In April 2021, Gartner surveyed more than 3,500 employees about a variety of topics. As Distinguished VP Analyst Helen Poitevin said, the survey:

> found that 40 percent of employees reported that they received no communication from their organization about what productivity data is collected and how it's being used. Plus, our research shows that even when there is communication on these topics, the quality is poor, resulting in limited employee understanding and awareness of personal data usage.[35]

Remote workers need to worry about more than their employers' prying eyes.

Gamification Revisited

As the previous chapter discussed, immersive technologies automatically collect oodles of data. By definition, they enable some degree of gamification.

In fairness, gamification isn't necessarily evil. Positive results may ensue, including increased transparency and employee performance. Those benefits frequently, though, come at a cost. Over-gamified environments can easily promote increased scrutiny, cutthroat mindsets among workers, decreased intrinsic motivation, and other undesirable outcomes. The *Black Mirror* episode "Nosedive" isn't so unrealistic after all.

What Happens Next?

Were he alive today, Taylor would doubtless approve of employee spyware and gamification. Less certain, though, is the percentage of knowledge workers who will be comfortable with increased levels of employer monitoring. A few interesting queries include:

- Is increased monitoring the cost of this relatively newfound flexibility? Do these fleas come with the dog?
- What percentage of employees will quit on general principle?
- How many will attempt to game the system using any number of techniques?

We'll see.

Predictions and Recommendations

How does all this shake out? What role should data and analytics play in evaluating employee performance? Should managers rely exclusively on their judgment and eschew all quantitative measures of employee performance? Is there a middle ground?

Companies will self-select into two camps. The first will continue to worship at the altar of W. Edwards Deming and his credo, "In God we trust. All others must bring data." Amazon may make a few tweaks at the edges, but you can't run a company anywhere near its scale without lots of numbers and standardized measures. Yeah, there are limits, but some level of employee monitoring is a necessary evil if you want reliable, same-day delivery.

The second group will recognize the limitations of excessive monitoring and analytics as a religion. These methods aren't just questionable and borderline intrusive; they're *counterproductive* in two ways. First, proving that you're busy reduces the time you can devote to your job. This kind of kabuki theatre is also infantilizing. Second, talented employees will head for the door.

Progressive managers and companies will do the hard work; they'll strike a balance between the qualitative and the quantitative. And make no mistake: finding a happy medium will be neither simple nor easy. As Jerry Muller writes in his 2018 book *The Tyranny of Metrics*:

> In the end, there is no silver bullet, no substitute for actually knowing one's subject and one's organization, which is partly a matter of experience and partly a matter of unquantifiable skill. Many matters of importance are too subject to judgment and interpretation to be solved by standardized metrics. Ultimately, the issue is not one of metrics versus judgment, but metrics as informing judgment, which includes knowing how much weight to give to metrics, recognizing their characteristic distortions,

and appreciating what can't be measured. In recent decades, too many politicians, business leaders, policymak-
ers, and academic officials have lost sight of that.

It's a tightrope. Monitor employees too tightly, and you'll irri-
tate them enough to leave. Give them free rein, and you'll invite
slacking. For now, be aware of the perils of both approaches. Review your metrics regularly. Adjust your dashboards and OKRs.
It's a mistake to set it and forget it.

On a different level, turnover among middle managers has
been staggering. These folks are caught in the crossfire. Their bosses are demanding one thing, and their underlings are having none
of it. As a result, they're miserable and, as a cohort, the most susceptible to burnout.[36]

Expect their flood of resignation letters to continue. The word
untenable comes to mind.

Key Points

- The use—and misuse—of tech and data to monitor employee productivity is anything but new. Since the pandemic, more companies have started spying on their employees.
- Frederick Taylor may have perished, but his influence is
  alive and well.
- Predictably, employees are finding creative workarounds
  to their bosses' requirements that they regularly prove
  their productivity.
- When a measure becomes a target, it ceases to be a good
  measure.

$$^x/_y$$

CHAPTER 9
Fractions

Say goodbye to binaries and hello to halves, thirds, and quarters.

"There are only two ways to make money in business: one is to bundle; the other is unbundle."
—JIM BARKSDALE

In the annals of technology, 1986 was an especially pivotal year. The personal computer was starting to move beyond its status as a niche product. Microsoft had released version 1.0 of its Windows operating system the previous November. That year, the Computer Museum in Boston asked a simple question: what was the first PC?

In the ensuing contest, judges landed on an oddly named device called a *Kenbak-1*.[1] John Blankenbaker and his Kenbak Corporation built the machine in 1971.

When it comes to contemporary processing power, the Kenbak-1 didn't exactly pack a wallop. It shipped with 256 *bytes* of memory. Not gigabytes or even megabytes. Bytes. (Proper microprocessors would arrive later that year.) The unit cost about $750 then and, accounting for inflation, would run you about $5,200 today. Kenbak ultimately manufactured fewer than 50 of them.[2]

Although it represented quite the achievement at the time, the standalone unit was expensive, difficult to find, and light on juice. That mix didn't appeal to young techies interested in learning about computers.

People like Bill Gates.

In his 2009 bestseller *Outliers: The Story of Success*, Malcolm Gladwell tells the tale of the precocious teenage computer geek. In 1967, his parents enrolled him in Lakeside, an exclusive private school in Seattle. In Gladwell's words:

> The school didn't have its students learn programming by the laborious computer-card system, like virtually everyone else was doing in the 1960s. Instead, Lakeside installed what was called an ASR-33 Teletype, which was a time-sharing terminal with a direct link to a mainframe computer in downtown Seattle.* "The whole idea of time-sharing only got invented in nineteen sixty-five," Gates continued. "Someone was pretty forward-looking."

Thanks to this happenstance, Bill Gates was one of the few people in the world able to do real-time programming in 1968. He was thirteen. The rest, of course, is history.

---

* Watch a demo of it yourself at https://tinyurl.com/9-asr-demo.

Fractions Everywhere

Most professionals these days don't share their computers, although the concept of fractions in computing is far from dead. Amazon built its massive cloud-computing business on the idea that companies should only purchase compute power on an as-needed basis. Salesforce pioneered the software-as-a-service business model in 1999. Why buy a suite of tools when you only use a few? Shelfware sucks.

Investors no longer need to buy whole shares of a company's stock. Using Robinhood[3] or Schwab, anyone can acquire fractional shares of $AMZN, $MSFT, $GE, or any publicly traded company.

Looking to procure only 2 percent of a blue-chip painting or a unique collectible, such as a 1986–87 Fleer Michael Jordan rookie card? Masterworks, Otis, and other companies facilitate these transactions.

Owning *part* of a domicile is hardly new. Thirteenth-century French castles represented some of the first shared abodes.[4] In the 1960s, resort timeshares popped up in Europe and then Hawaii. In 1984, Marriott launched its Vacation Club. Hilton and other large hotel chains followed with similar offerings.

Today, the Bay Area startup Pacaso offers a decidedly modern take on communal home ownership. It provides the ability to purchase a fractional interest in second residences. Unlike a traditional resort timeshare, though, a Pacaso customer who purchases a fraction of a property receives a deed.[5] (And, yes, they can complete the transaction via blockchain-based cryptocurrencies. Proving that you own one-fifth of a multimillion-dollar dwelling is probably wise.[6])

It's an innovative business model, but some groups aren't thrilled with it. In California, Napa and Sonoma County residents have started petitions and even taken legal action to put the kibosh on Pacaso's ambitions in the North Bay.[7]

There's an underlying thread here. Fractions are having their moment, and they're coming to workplaces as well.

Fractional Offices

Beginning in the 1980s, commercial developers upped the rate at which they built offices. As for the reasons, interest rates were low. The generous federal tax breaks of the Reagan era encouraged investment, and businesses promptly took advantage of them. The office-construction boom continued in the 1990s. The dot-com boom and its unprofitable, misguided startups artificially boosted demand for a swanky new workspace.

Today, it's clear that developers got ahead of their skis in some cities.[8] The overdevelopment problem existed well before March 2020. The pandemic—and second-order effects like the rise of remote work—merely shined a light on the issue.

While there's an excess of one type of available square footage in the US, there's an outright dearth in another.

Mike Kingsella is the CEO of Up for Growth, a nonprofit "committed to solving the housing shortage and affordability crisis through data-driven research and evidence-based policy."[9] As he told NPR in July 2022:

> We're seeing a shortage, or housing underproduction, in all corners of the US. America's fallen 3.8 million homes short of meeting housing needs. And that's both rental housing and ownership.[10]

You don't have to be a real estate tycoon like Stephen Ross to see what happens next.

An Equilibrium Emerges Over Where We Work

Despite the chaos of the past eighteen months, a certain equilibrium has emerged concerning where we work. Gallup reported in August 2022 that four in five individuals who can do their jobs outside of a traditional office are doing so.[11] Interestingly, that rate has remained surprisingly consistent over that period. In other words, people have adapted to their new circumstances. As Figure 9.1 displays, employees have become comfortable working in different places.

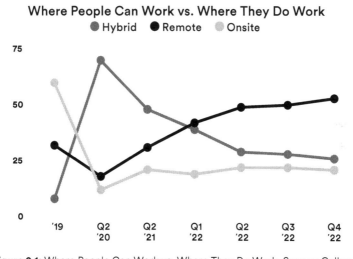

Figure 9.1: Where People Can Work vs. Where They Do Work, Source: Gallup

We're back to normal in one sense: traveling, attending sporting events, and dining at restaurants. Professionally speaking, the same isn't true: we trek to the office far less frequently than we did before the pandemic. Figure 9.2 shows how several prepandemic activities have resumed.

In-Person Activities Have (Mostly) Returned

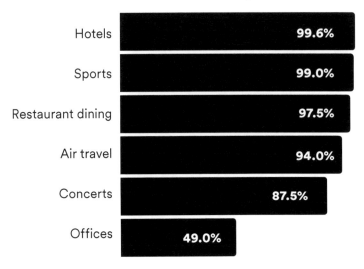

Data recorded at the end of November 2022.

Figure 9.2: In-Person Activities Have (Mostly) Returned, Source: STR (hotels), PredictHQ (sports and concerts), OpenTable (restaurants), Transportation Security Administration (air travel), and Kastle Systems (offices)

Recall from Chapter 2 that, when it comes to where they work, employees want a fair degree of *permanent* flexibility. They're willing to die on that hill. As more people refuse to revert to daily in-office work, something has to give.

Harsh New Realities Disrupt Commercial Real Estate

That *something* is commercial office space. Aggregate demand for offices will never rebound to its pre-COVID level. So says Joseph Gyourko—a real-estate professor at The Wharton School at the University of Pennsylvania. A flight to quality is likely, and a good portion of mid-tier buildings won't survive in their current form.[12]

So, what will all those least desirable edifices ultimately become? There's no single answer, but apartments represent an obvious option. As Natalie Wong writes for *Bloomberg*:

> New York developer Silverstein Properties is seeking to raise $1.5 billion for converting older offices to residential buildings.
>
> The landlord, known for developing towers at the World Trade Center, is in talks with investors to kick-start what could be a "$10 billion-plus" opportunity, Chief Executive Officer Marty Burger said in an interview. The firm is exploring acquisitions of Manhattan office buildings that are facing growing vacancies or debt burdens. The effort could potentially expand to other areas of the US, such as Washington, DC, Boston, and the West Coast.[13]

Silverstein isn't the only one thinking about converting proper offices to urban residences. San Francisco Mayor London Breed has spoken extensively about addressing the city's well-documented housing shortage by, in part, transforming commercial space into affordable housing.* Apartments have already supplanted office towers in downtown Calgary.[14]

But conversions to residential housing are complicated and expensive, notes Dror Poleg, an economic historian who researches technology's impact on how we work and live. As he wrote on his blog in December 2022:

> Most landlords are still waiting for the old normal to return. And most leases signed before 2019 have still not come

---

* Watch a CNBC segment with her on it at https://tinyurl.com/nine-ps-cnbc.

up for renewal. At some point in the next three years, the office market will reach a tipping point, and many more landlords will throw in the towel. This does not mean that all office buildings will suffer, but many of them will, and the result will be a relative avalanche of conversions of various kinds. Relative, because most office buildings are too hard or too costly to convert. But a sizable minority of the current supply can and will be converted.[15]

Poleg is right. For all sorts of reasons, it's neither economically nor logistically feasible to convert every redundant corporate headquarters into primo city apartments and condominiums.

That reality doesn't mean, though, that the space needs will be abandoned. On the contrary, schools, storage facilities, and health clubs are springing up. And why not rent that space to a movie or TV crew? Directors from *Succession* and *Billions* used floors of unoccupied offices to film recent episodes.[16]

Landlords aren't fools. They're well aware that millions of workers are demanding flexibility and refusing to revert to prepandemic daily commutes to the office.

Against this backdrop, it's absurd for them to expect their existing tenants to sign new ten-year leases after their current ones lapse, even if the latter can negotiate favorable terms.

The Future Workplace Is Fractional and Flexible

Instead, commercial real estate brokers and landlords are wisely—if sometimes reluctantly—exploring flexible alternatives to rent their space. (Each day that a building goes unrented represents lost income for its owner.)

While existing players figure out their next steps and tweak longstanding business models, ambitious startups smell opportunity and are predictably starting to pounce. For example, San Francisco-based Codi company offers:

> what amounts to a time-share for office tenants by pairing small companies with hybrid schedules so they use the same space on alternate days during a typical week. The business, which manages about 50 locations in the Bay Area and New York, has grown 40 percent in the last six months.[17]

Speaking with *SF Standard,* CEO Christelle Rohaut aptly describes why commercial real estate won't revert to its 2019 state:

> The workplace is going through a massive shift, and companies more than ever value ease and speed and flexibility. The traditional office experience does not offer that.[18]

Compared to garden-variety commercial leases, Codi allows more flexible and affordable terms. Clients looking to customize their square footage can do so as well. In September 2022, the startup raised $16 million in Series A funding from Andreessen Horowitz.[19] (Yes, that's the very same Marc Andreessen we met in Chapter 6.)

Startups like Codi can offer the equivalent of joint custody of a building or floor. It's not hard to envision Company A inhabiting a workspace every Monday, Wednesday, and Friday, while Company B takes Tuesday and Thursday. Other organizations may alternate mornings and afternoons. What about swapping every other week or month? Beyond times and dates, Codi offers flexible locations. Start multiplying, and the possibilities swiftly become limitless.

Let's return to traditional landlords. How will they react when all those pre-COVID leases elapse?

In the past, some landlords weren't flexible for one simple reason: they didn't need to be. As such, they bristled at multiple-tenant leases. If you drove past an open building in 2018, you wouldn't likely see a "Will Divide" sign. As a lot, expect landlords to be more amenable to flexibility and fractions in the future.

Does this mean that *every* organization will eventually demand extreme flexibility from its landlord? Will all companies part with their own headquarters?

Of course not. Plenty will want to own and maintain full-time, permanent digs. We saw this in Chapter 2. Cisco, LinkedIn, and Dropbox all spent considerable funds reimagining their corporate headquarters for the hybrid future of work. In other words, these weren't short-term moves.

The Money Motive

Still, expect the rise of creative, flexible, and fractional office arrangements to continue indefinitely. Forget employee preferences for a moment. There's too great a financial incentive for organizations *not* to rethink their real estate footprints.

Waste has been rampant for years. A 2014 Accenture report found that:

> Few companies have performed a truly strategic analysis of the real estate portfolio, but the amount of waste is significant, and the pay-off from rightsizing a portfolio could be substantial. Shedding excess real estate is the first force multiplier, yielding cash flow benefits from the asset sale, and delivering ongoing benefits by eliminating

the $40 of ongoing annual operating costs for every $100 of real estate.[20]

And real estate inefficiencies continue to cost businesses big money. The company Density measures workplace usage and helps its clients optimize their real estate expenditures. In 2022, Density released the results of a study of two thousand workspaces. They were empty for more than a third of working hours.[21]

Fractional Employment

Organizations have long supplemented their full-time workforces with all sorts of contingent labor. For example, few laypersons realize how much colleges and universities rely on adjunct professors. As the American Federation of Teachers reported in 2022:

> Forty years ago, 70 percent of academic employees were tenured or on the tenure track. Today, that figure has flipped; 75 percent of faculty are not eligible for tenure, and 47 percent hold part-time positions.[22]

Why the dramatic shift?

Money, of course.

More than half of the respondents in a 2020 survey earned less than $3,500 per course.[23] Adjuncts who teach five courses each semester struggle to scrape by. (If you believe that all your kid's professors have landed cushy jobs, read Herb Childress's book *The Adjunct Underclass*.)

Adjunct pay isn't just woeful; it may be illegal. Factor in the time that contingent faculty members spend preparing materials, grading, and holding office hours, and many earn less than minimum wage. Now think about the rate at which schools have increased tuition relative to inflation over the past four decades[24] and administrators' bloated salaries.[25] How American institutions of higher education pay the majority of their professors is disgraceful.

Beyond Academia

Moving to the tech world, even the most affluent companies routinely augment their staff with temps and independent contractors. (Chapter 1 began with the story of the mass walkout at Google. Not all who protested could, legally speaking, call Google their *employer*.) Facebook has paid Accenture upward of $500 million annually to provide additional personnel to scrub toxic content from its site.[26]

For their part, consultancies remain lean by using subcontractors after landing new clients and engagements. (I regularly served as a sub during the aughts.) As mentioned in Chapter 7, Uber, Lyft, and other gig economy companies have spent hundreds of millions of dollars to thwart referenda mandating that they classify their workforces as *employees*.

The specific nomenclature of contingent workers varies, but the underlying principle remains the same. Pay individual wages—and only *wages*—when you need more human hands. This fractional arrangement allows organizations to eschew employment benefits that can approach 50 percent of an employee's annual salary.[27] The practice is concurrently several things: universal, understandable, hyper-efficient, logical, and often ethically questionable.

Moving Up the Ladder: The Rise of the Fractional CXO

Hybrid and remote work mean that executives are reevaluating whether they need permanent, full-time offices. Small and midsized firms are starting to ask the same question about certain senior roles. As a result, the idea of using contingent workers is beginning to permeate higher rungs of the corporate ladder. We're seeing the gradual arrival of the fractional chief executive.

In fairness, you're unlikely to find a longstanding fractional executive at a Fortune 500 company. (Yes, sometimes unexpected retirements and disciplinary issues force corporations to appoint temporary replacements. For the most part, though, these are interim assignments.)

Fractional executives are experienced hired guns who, for whatever reason, need to right an organization's ship. The best ones can immediately hit the ground running, identify thorny internal problems, chart a path to resolution, and oversee its execution. Unlike their consulting counterparts, fractional executives are fully embedded and accountable members of their leadership teams; they're in it for the long term.

Ken Weil has served as a fractional chief financial officer for dozens of companies over the past fifteen years. Researching this book, I spoke extensively with him. Weil offers several reasons that fractional CFOs are becoming more popular, some of which apply to other business functions.

Business Need

Some startups simply aren't mature enough to need the talents of a full-time CFO. Beyond that, there are financial factors to consider. Founders or investors may lack the desire to award equity grants to new executives. Beyond that, it's often difficult for a new venture to justify a $250,000 salary at such an embryonic stage.

At the same time, there are only so many hats that even the most intelligent, accomplished, and efficient business leader can effectively wear. (Elon Musk seems to have learned this lesson the hard way with Twitter.) A fractional CFO lets other executives stick to their knitting. For example, a COO need not pretend to possess the skills of a CIO and vice versa.

As Weil explained, his clients hire him because they frequently face a complicated tax or accounting issue that their current leadership team has never confronted. In these cases, the costs of winging it far exceed his fee.

In a way, fractional leaders aren't all that different from their full-time counterparts. Karina Mikhli is a fractional COO and the founder of Fractionals United. When I spoke to her, she emphasized the parallels between full-time and fractional COO roles. No two are alike; each must complement what the founder or CEO needs.

Executive Turnover Spikes

Thirty-seven CFOs stepped down from S&P 500 companies in 2020. That number represents an increase of 27.6 percent from the previous year.[28] And this was *before* the Great Resignation arrived in earnest.

The Current Labor Market

Chapter 1 covered why the historically low unemployment rate is likely to persist. Because of it, some firms simply can't find the right candidates for senior positions. All things considered,

Chapter 9 Fractions

209

hiring a fractional CFO might represent the best option at the time. What's more, a six-month contract locks in a talented, experienced individual and provides a modicum of certainty.

The Widespread Acceptance of Remote Work

During our extended chat, Weil told me that, for specific clients, he used to spend upward of three hours per day commuting. During the early days of the pandemic, some of his clients forbade him from coming to the office. Travel restrictions ultimately eased, but Weil mostly kept working from home. As the immersive technologies detailed in Chapter 7 mature, expect the need for employees' constant physical presence to abate further.

Recall from Chapter 2 one of the chief benefits of dispersed workforces: companies increase the available talent pool. The same principle applies here.

Peering Into the Future

The same incentives to hire fractional CFOs exist for other business functions, especially as a firm grows. That's not to say that you'll see a proliferation of part-time company presidents or CEOs, but chief technology and legal officers are prime candidates for fractional status. With respect to the latter, a successful startup that hires a *de facto* head of legal simultaneously fulfills a critical business need while saving money. As but one example, consider AI and copyright issues, discussed in Chapter 5. This type of fractional and mutually beneficial arrangement can pay off in spades, especially as these companies continue to flourish.

Chapter 1 discussed the heads that Amazon, Meta, and other tech behemoths have scalped over the past year. By way of review and since the pandemic began, businesses that employ fewer than

250 people have *added* 3.67 million jobs. These numbers in part explain the historically strong labor market. For the purposes of this chapter, this trend bodes well for the future for fractional chief executives.

In January 2023, Microsoft announced ten thousand layoffs. CFO Amy Hood wasn't one of them.[29] Nor did her employer relegate her to fractional status. You need not have studied finance in college to know that a public company with roughly two hundred thousand employees and a market cap hovering around $2 trillion needs a full-time CFO.

Say, however, that three thousand of those affected employees find jobs at growing shops approaching $30 million in sales. These are exactly the types of businesses that would benefit from someone like Ken Weil. In a similar vein, the company that graduates from QuickBooks to NetSuite might need to find a fractional CIO.

Key Points

- In the next few years, millions of square feet of office space will become apartments, gyms, and schools.
- Employee work preferences, technological advancements, and financial necessity are causing an increasing number of organizations to rethink the need for full-time, dedicated offices and rigid ten-year leases.
- A confluence of trends, including a shift from big to small, portends a strong future for fractional chief executives.

CHAPTER 10

Navigating the Path Forward

Organizational change, the nine, and strategies for an uncertain future.

"In the midst of chaos, there is also opportunity."

—SUN TZU

The 1976 film *All the President's Men* is a classic. Dustin Hoffman and Robert Redford star as *Washington Post* reporters Carl Bernstein and Bob Woodward, respectively. The duo meticulously investigates the June 1972 break-in of the Democratic National Committee headquarters at the Watergate Office Building in Washington, DC. The team's reporting ultimately led to a slew of arrests and convictions. Oh, and the resignation of President Richard Nixon on August 8, 1974.

Watch the movie today. Depending on your age, you'll barely recognize how the two iconic journalists broke stories. Forget 70s-era fashion, although *Mad Men* temporarily resurrected it in the past decade. Consider the tools that Bernstein and Woodward used at the time: landlines, typewriters, pens, notepads, and in-person meetings. Ultimately, their work appeared in a physical form. Yes, I'm talking about newspapers.

Reluctant Newspapers Ignore Tectonic Forces

In hindsight, that era may have represented the golden age for reporters and reporting. As always, new technologies arrived, but newspaper leadership and journalists generally found them manageable and even beneficial. Desktop computers replaced typewriters. Telexes, pagers, fax machines, and early cell phones inarguably made reporters' jobs easier.

Powerful forces started gaining momentum in 1995. Those forces ultimately annihilated the industry and caused hundreds of papers to close shop.

Technology Morphs From Friend to Enemy

There's no sense in sugarcoating it: the explosion of the web in the mid-1990s caught newspapers flatfooted. Craig Newmark launched Craigslist, a remarkably plain and simple site that would siphon off want ads and job postings from local papers. In 2006, total revenue from US newspapers hit $49.3 billion, recovering nicely from the dot-com implosion. The reprieve, however, turned out to be short-lived. Pew Research estimated that, by 2020, the figure had plunged to $10 billion—an 80 percent drop.[1]

When hidebound newspaper editors finally recognized the need to adapt, the die had been cast. Local presses struggled to keep the lights on. To get a sense of the drama behind the scenes, check out the final season of David Simon's groundbreaking series *The Wire*. It depicts a fictionalized version of the *Baltimore Sun*, Maryland's largest general-circulation daily newspaper at the time. Fifteen years after its denouement, *The Wire* remains an important cultural artifact.

Hundreds of papers ultimately shuttered. In 2019, the Associated Press reported that more than 1,400 American cities and towns had lost newspapers in the past fifteen years alone.[2] Then came COVID-19. The pandemic caused hundreds more to close their doors for good.[3] Talk about adding salt to the wound.

As an interesting aside, Newmark publicly donated $20 million to The City University of New York Graduate School of Journalism in June 2018.[4] Newmark spoke about the need to advance quality journalism and to provide opportunities to people who might not otherwise get them. Both are worthy goals, and I applaud them. Still, I suspect that the prodigious sum also represented a form of penance. (Newmark is no idiot. He must recognize the irreparable damage that his company wrought on modern journalism.)

Now, no rational person would place all the industry's blame at the feet of Newmark or "the internet." (If not for Newmark, someone else invariably would have created a Craigslist facsimile, albeit under a different name.) To be sure, many individual newspapers' wounds were self-inflicted. Plenty of prominent old-school executives and editors fought emerging technologies and new business models. Some made distribution deals with the devil (re: Facebook or Google), only to regret them years later.

There's no other way to say it: journalism has undergone a sea change in the past three decades, a point that the following two examples illustrate.

Andrew Ross Sorkin of CNBC and the *New York Times* interviewed Netflix cofounder and, at the time,[*] co-CEO Reed Hastings at the November 2022 DealBook Conference.[†] The journalist peppered Hastings on several topics, including threats to the streaming giant's business model from deep-pocketed competitors and free, user-generated content from YouTube and TikTok. Here's a snippet from their amicable but colorful back-and-forth:

> **Hastings:** Twenty years ago, you could make a business of selling yesterday's news, and that was a big business.
>
> **Sorkin:** Whoa! The gloves come off in the opposite direction.
>
> **Hastings:** Now, that's not a viable business model, right?

Hasting was spot-on, and Sorkin, one of the world's most respected financial journalists, damn well knew it.

Amazon cofounder and former CEO Jeff Bezos bought the *Washington Post* in August 2013 for $250 million. (Yes, the very same one.)

Unlike Elon Musk's reluctant and disastrous Twitter acquisition, Bezos wasn't searching for a shiny new thing. He understood the grave—even dystopian—ramifications of a society bereft of reputable journalism and journalists.

---

* Hastings stepped down from the role on January 19, 2022.
† Watch it yourself at https://tinyurl.com/db-hastings.

Society Suffers

Dismiss local newspapers as dinosaurs if you want, but it's a mistake. They still serve an essential societal function.

As but one recent example, consider the *North Shore Leader*, an admittedly small publication that bills itself as "The Leading News Source for Long Island's Gold Coast."

Before the November 2022 congressional elections, *The Leader* extensively reported on the veracity of claims made by George Santos, a Republican running for Congress in New York's third congressional district. Unfortunately, more prominent media outlets largely ignored its coverage.

After Santos won, more media outlets picked up the paper's stories, and a brouhaha ensued. The *New York Times* reported that "he seems to have misrepresented a number of his career highlights."[5] Santos himself copped to "lying about his professional background, educational history, and property ownership."[6] You know, little things. Santos doesn't intend to vacate his newly won seat.

In January, the Campaign Legal Center, a nonpartisan ethics watchdog, filed a complaint with the Federal Elections Commission, alleging that Santos violated campaign finance laws.[7] Count Texas Rep. Kevin Brady among the principled Republicans who believe that the Congressional-elect should step down to avert further staining Abraham Lincoln's party.[8]

And what about all other scandals that remain underreported or unreported altogether? Who would want to live in such a world? ProPublica can only do so much. Perhaps that's why Bezos's Blue Origin is exploring private space travel.

For journalists, the hits just keep on coming. In another terrifying trend, public figures, business leaders, and even national politicians are increasingly attacking the institution of journalism, individual outlets, and even proper journalists.

Bloodied but Still Standing

Zooming out for a moment, journalism may be battered, but at least the profession is still standing. Formerly sizable behemoths and even entire industries have come and gone in the past fifty years. (Cue obligatory Blockbuster, Research in Motion, Tower Records, and Borders references.)

Reporters still break stories. Beginning in 2016, proper journalism even experienced a bit of a revival. #factsmatter Due mainly to technology, however, its business looks nothing like the early 1990s, never mind the 1970s. And the same holds for newsrooms themselves.

In 2012, HBO released *The Newsroom*, the Aaron Sorkin series about the fictional TV network Atlantis Cable News. Jeff Daniels stars as ACN anchor Will McAvoy, and his rant to open the series continues to amaze me a decade later.[*]

Unlike WaPo, ACN didn't create a physical product. It produced 24/7 TV news. Think bits, not atoms. Not surprisingly, throughout the series, you won't find any landlines, typewriters, or fax machines throughout all three seasons. In their stead, smartphones, Twitter feeds, websites, powerful computers, and high-definition TV scrolls permeate the set.

ACN may have been a figment of Sorkin's imagination, but it wasn't unrealistic. On the contrary, the show nails the innards of the modern-day newsroom. It's downright unrecognizable from the WaPo headquarters profiled in *All the President's Men*.

---

[*] Watch it yourself at https://tinyurl.com/ps-newsroom.

Some real twentieth-century news outlets defied the odds, absorbed some body blows, and emerged standing. They successfully weathered the technology and economic storms of the twenty-first century. To do so, they had to stare into the abyss, ask existential questions, embrace new ways of thinking, and make massive operational and strategic shifts.

Business leaders are facing a similar inflection point. Ignoring the powerful forces discussed in this book all but guarantees obsolescence, irrelevance, and even extinction.

Coping With the Nine: Six Options

Nine tectonic forces are fundamentally altering how, when, and where we work. Unlike the changes that rocked the newspaper industry, these forces are playing out much faster. They're *already* upending myriad workplaces. As we've seen, some organizations are unrecognizable from their prepandemic counterparts on several levels.

As the pandemic recedes (hopefully for good), business leaders must ask big, hairy questions. Examples include:

- What kind of company do you want to run?
- Are you willing to question everything and adopt a very different management mindset?
- Will your actions truly match your words, or will you just pay lip service to new norms?
- Do you just want to run out the clock until retirement?

I mentioned in the Preface that this book covered a great deal of ground. It's finally time to discuss options for proceeding.

1. Ignore Reality

Maybe the forces described in this book have overwhelmed you. Why not ignore them?

Refusing to accept the post-COVID world of work won't make it go away. Ditto for temporarily ignoring the nine forces. As C. S. Lewis famously quipped, "Denial is the shock absorber for the soul. It protects us until we are equipped to cope with reality."

At some point soon, you'll have to face the music.

2. Try to Turn Back the Clock

The prepandemic workplace was so much simpler. Why not bring it back?

The leaders who try to revert to 2019 will fail. Despite the advances in AI and automation we've seen in these pages, they still need human beings, and therein lies the problem. (Well, except if you run a McDonald's in Fort Worth, Texas.)

Regressive organizations will see a sustained talent drain that will ultimately decimate them. Rockstars will easily find more flexible, greener pastures. Raj Choudhury, a prominent economist and professor at Harvard Business School, spoke to *Wired* in December 2022:

> There are two kinds of companies. One is going to embrace work-from-anywhere, and the second is in denial—I feel those companies will lose their workforce. Companies that are trying to drag back time will lose some of their best talent, and that dynamic will force these companies to catch up.[9]

No argument here. Over time, the mass employee exodus will leave complacent organizations with only poor or mediocre performers, exacerbating their downward spirals. To quote the late Steve Jobs, "A-players attract A-players. B-players attract C-players." Some CEOs have attempted to purge newly empowered, "woke" employees. Good luck with that. A July 2021 poll from Vox and Data for Progress revealed that 89 percent of Democrats approve of remote work. The number for Republicans was 81 percent.[10]

3. Get a Little Bit Pregnant

None of the nine forces is binary; there are levels of WFH and analytics. By the same token, think of automation, AR, VR, and generative AI as dials, not switches.

Dipping your toe in the water might seem like a safe, palatable solution. Why not compromise? Throw employees a bone and let them work from home one day every other week. Hope that it works. Form a task force. Promise to investigate the viability of blockchain at some point in the next five years while secretly hoping you won't have to do anything with it. Why not try half-measures?

Two reasons make me skeptical. First, newspapers adopted a similar Pollyannaish approach, and we know how it turned out for them. Second, as Rick Page's 2002 book reminds us, hope is not a strategy.

4. Scale Back Operations

Iconic magazines have opted to go this route over the past decade. In October 2012, *Newsweek* ceased its print edition after eighty years.[11] In November 2022, the *Washington Post* pulled the plug on its Sunday magazine.[12] Scour the newsstands all you want, but you won't find *Entertainment Weekly* anymore. Barnes and Noble announced that it would stop selling new magazines early in the pandemic.[13] For their part, many newspapers significantly down-scaled, moving from a daily publishing schedule to a weekly one.

Scaling back is a tough pill for most businessfolk to swallow. After all, isn't bigger, better, faster, and more the whole point of capitalism?* Apart from forced reductions, has any company willingly rejected this mindset and shrunk?

As a matter of fact, yes.

Read the 2007 book *Small Giants: Companies That Choose to Be Great Instead of Big*. Bo Burlingham details firms that intentionally contracted their operations. In so doing, they returned to simpler, more intimate work environments. In each case, management rejected a growth-at-all-costs mindset—and was glad it did.

The same option exists today.

5. Tap Out

Generative AI? Blockchain? Fractional offices and leadership? RTO and WFH? WTF?

Making sense of the post-COVID workplace hasn't been easy, never mind successfully adapting to it. This new world isn't everyone's jam. There's no shame in admitting that the workplace of today and tomorrow is just too *weird*.

Maybe your attempts to revert to the 2019 workplace have left you exhausted. You've realized that this approach is futile. What to do?

Stop trying to swim against the stream and, if your circumstances allow, gracefully exit. If retiring early isn't in the cards, simply hit pause. Take an extended sabbatical if you can afford it. If you can't, get a side hustle and think long and hard. What

---

* Hat tip to the title of the 1994 album by 4 Non Blondes.

company, field, or vocation suits your temperament? You certainly wouldn't be the first to call time out.

6. Steer Into the Skid

For different reasons, the first four options may not appeal to you and early retirement, option 5, isn't feasible. You need to stay in the game, but you realize the futility of attempting to thwart progress and change. You don't want to spend the rest of your career trying to roll back employee flexibility and empowerment. Why resist useful and inevitable technologies?

You've met your share of old-school founders and presidents. You just don't fancy yourself a reactionary type. The idea of working for—much less leading—an organization trying to turn back time doesn't sit well with you.

If the stories of the organizations in the previous chapters inspired or intrigued you, I've got good news: they're not alone. Other open-minded and enlightened leaders have effectively read the room. They correctly believe that they're sitting at the precipice of a unique, once-in-a-generation opportunity to do the following:

- Reimagine work.
- Forge long-term bonds with their workforces.
- Attract talented employees by building a unique brand.
- Embrace a new wave of powerful technologies.
- Improve manual processes.
- And much more.

Why not rip off the Band-Aid and start now?

In other words, rather than fight the forces, embrace them.

Pulling It Off

Steering into the skid offers the most upside, but harbor no illusions: it's also the most daunting to pull off.* Specifically, it presents considerable logistical, technological, and financial challenges.

Keep these obstacles in mind, but don't let them deter you. Here are some recommendations on how to proceed with Option 6.

Realize the Benefits of Zigging While Others Zag

We've seen this movie before. (See the newspaper industry mentioned earlier.) Business leaders arrogantly think they can successfully revert to earlier times.

Of course, they're deluding themselves. In the long term, almost all will fail—some in spectacular fashion. They're virtually guaranteeing that their firms will eventually suffer the same unfortunate fates as storied periodicals such as the *Green Bay News-Chronicle* and the *New York Sun*.

While unfortunate, this misguided mindset represents an enormous opportunity for the business leaders who get it. Take advantage of your competitors' intractability. Zig while everyone else zags. Progressive organizations regularly do.

It's time to review the fascinating work of Zeynep Ton, currently a professor at the MIT Sloan School of Management. I'm referring to her 2014 book *The Good Jobs Strategy: How the Smartest Companies Invest in Employees to Lower Costs and Boost Profit*.

Ton details the employee-friendly business practices of Costco, QuikTrip, Home Depot, Trader Joe's, and others. They include

---

* To steal a line from *The Shawshank Redemption*, "If you're reading this, you've gotten out. And if you've come this far, maybe you're willing to come a little further."

paying above-market wages, *over*staffing, and cross-training. Concerning the latter, she writes:

> Cross-training ... expresses the realization that employees are human beings and that most human beings are capable of many different things and aspire to do great things, even if on a small scale.

Unfortunately, Ton's research suggests that these firms represent the exception that proves the rule. Old-school retailers have routinely skimped on labor expenses, and the results have been unsurprisingly disastrous. Circuit City serves as a cautionary tale.

A Tale of Two Retailers

By 2007, ecommerce had recovered from the depths of the dot-bomb bust. People liked the convenience of purchasing an increasing array of items from their computers and, in the coming years, from their smartphones. As always, though, success wasn't evenly distributed.

Big-box retailer Circuit City was gasping for air. Amazon and the related practice of showrooming (mentioned in Chapter 3) were battering brick-and-mortar retailers. In response CEO Phil Schoonover canned 3,400 of its veteran, more expensive workers in March 2007. In their stead, he hired lower paid and lower skilled ones.[14]

The gambit soon backfired. As Rachel Beck of the Associated Press described at the time:

> Too bad that service matters in that corner of the retail market. Shoppers quickly noticed and fled—leaving Circuit City's sales and profit plunging. Its same-store holiday sales, reported on Monday, fell 11.4 percent. And its

stock is now about 80 percent below where it was the day
before it made the staffing announcement.[15]

Less than two years later, the company predictably filed for
bankruptcy.

Contrast Circuit City's strategy and results with those of another large retailer. Best Buy faced the same retail environment,
financial pressures, and existential threat from Amazon. Instead of
downsizing veteran workers, it heavily invested in them. Best Buy's
leadership wisely doubled down on service. Geek Squad became
its secret weapon.[16] It was not only able to survive but thrive. Over
a decade after its risky gambit, *Barron's* named it the most sustainable US company.[17]

David Takes on Goliath

More recently, Shopify has taken a similar tact against Amazon. Both marketplaces offer their third-party sellers robust ecommerce tools and fulfillment services. Their approaches, though, are
anything but identical.

Amazon frequently launches private label brands to compete
directly against sellers on its marketplace. Can someone say *frene-
my*? The company's methods may not exactly be legal. In July 2020,
then-CEO Jeff Bezos testified before Congress about the matter.
Amazon may have unfairly used proprietary data to compete with
its merchants.[18] Under oath, Bezos couldn't rule it out.

Shopify's seller-friendly approach lets merchants create spiffy
websites, own their customer relationships, and keep their data.
Oh, and the company doesn't launch competing products.

The strategy is making inroads. Shopify's revenue in 2021 surpassed $4.6 billion, a threefold jump from 2019.[19]

Recognize the Complexity of the Endeavor

Profound organizational change is possible, but only a buffoon would call it *easy*. What's more, one size has *never* fit all. The same tenet holds here.

Moreover, our conventions around work evolved over decades. You don't just hit a switch and magically create a new, perfect workplace. It takes time. Don't try to boil the ocean.

Recognize the folly of one-size-fits-all. Tactics that *seem* to work for a small tech startup or chic design firm probably won't fly at bureaucratic, mature healthcare organizations and financial institutions. Different regulations, company cultures, employee skillsets, business environments, and personality types pose vastly different challenges.

Expect Some Turbulence

Don't confuse steering into the skid with smooth sailing. Expect some unanticipated bumps along the way.

For example, adopting employee-friendly policies doesn't guarantee annual profits or short-term labor peace. Exhibit A: Trader Joe's, one of the companies profiled in *The Good Jobs Strategy*. In the summer of 2022, employees at stores in Western Massachusetts and Minneapolis voted for collective representation. Workers allege that "the company has violated labor laws in trying to prevent further stores from unionizing."[20]

Prioritize Stakeholders, Not Just Shareholders

We've seen how nine powerful and inexorable forces are reshaping the workplace. Most organizations will struggle to adapt to this wildly new world of work. Navigating the present and future will require senior leaders to ask and answer fundamental questions.

Let's return to the subject of Chapter 1: the empowered employee. Are managers *required* to placate their workforces?

No lesser authority than Nobel laureate Milton Friedman said *no*. He famously argued that "the social responsibility of business is to increase its profits."[21] If that means minimizing the concerns of their workforce or society at large, so be it. More than fifty years after uttering those words, countless chief executives believe that, above all else, they're legally obligated to "maximize corporate profits and 'shareholder value.'"[22]

Legally speaking, that popular refrain just doesn't hold water. I'll defer to the US Supreme Court. It has ruled that "modern corporate law does not require for-profit corporations to pursue profit at the expense of everything else, and many do not."

How do you reform institutions that have long prioritized shareholders above all their other constituencies? It's not easy, but we've taken a significant step. The influential Business Roundtable in August 2019 did something extraordinary: it changed its definition of a corporation's raison d'être. From its website:

181 CEOs of America's largest corporations overturned a 22-year-old policy statement that defined a corporation's principal purpose as maximizing shareholder return.

In its place, the CEOs of Business Roundtable adopted a new Statement on the Purpose of a Corporation declaring that companies should serve not only their shareholders, but also deliver value to their customers, invest in employees, deal fairly with suppliers, and support the communities in which they operate.[23]

Yes, making money is important. Kudos to the Business Roundtable for formally and finally recognizing that it should *not* represent an enterprise's singular focus or objective.

Consider a New Legal Structure

The management team that wants to reorient its corporate priorities need not adopt a new legal corporate structure. Plenty of enterprises, however, have done just that. Beginning in 2007, the number of Certified B Corporations started rising.

By 2016, more than 1,700 corporations in fifty countries had received the certification.[24] As of this writing, there are over 6,000 in more than eighty countries and over 150 industries.[25]

B corps often attract talented, like-minded employees by encouraging social responsibility.[26] In some instances, they've accepted submarket wages precisely because they believe in their employer's missions.

Reimagine Human Resources

For a long time now, the formal charter of the garden-variety HR department has been to attract, retain, and motivate employees. (Although not nearly as sexy, it also serves as the police department when employees break bad.)

HR's job has never been easy, but it's nearly impossible now. HR folks are trying to navigate a backdrop of uneven corporate return-to-work policies, stressed employees, increased employee empowerment, the explosion of remote and hybrid work, the Great Resignation, and a tight labor market.

Is it surprising that HR managers, recruiters, and compensation analysts are increasingly quitting? I'm not talking about quiet quitting either. LinkedIn reported in June 2022 that HR employees are leaving at the highest rate of all job functions—nearly 15 percent over the past year.[27]

In Chapter 8, I referenced some companies that have ditched formal employee performance reviews. It's time for chief people officers to ask themselves a few fundamental questions:

- How does this process *really* benefit the organization and its employees?
- Is this the best use of everyone's time?

And, no, maintaining tradition doesn't qualify as an acceptable answer.

Why not *finally* shift HR's focus from primarily administrative tasks like these to more valuable, strategic ones? Remote/hybrid work is downright essential these days. How can HR make it more effective? What about helping managers become more than just delegators, rule-enforcers, and expense-report approvers?

The need to redefine the roles and responsibilities of managers is here. So says Brian Kropp, managing director at Accenture. In his words:

> Managers going forward are going to be less technical experts and more social-emotional experts, to help employees navigate the culture of the organization.[28]

But HR can't do it alone. Better equipping workplaces and organizations for the future won't happen without the contributions of another critical constituency.

Level-Up Information Technology

For Option 6 to work, IT leaders and departments must up their games. Big time. Blockchain, mixed reality, robotic process automation, and other rapidly emerging technologies are doing more than just making employees more productive; they're making contemporary work possible.

Expecting employees to independently figure out rapidly evolving technologies is an abdication of IT's responsibility. IT needs to do more than merely respond to employee helpdesk calls, block websites, and the like. There's a massive opportunity—nay, *requirement*—for IT to truly lead and show its moxie.

If you're skeptical, ask yourself which is more valuable: HR as the police department or as a true business partner.

Parting Advice

Let's put a bow on this book with some final recommendations.

Charting a Course

To me, the path forward is ultimately a Hobson's choice. I'll argue for Option 6 until I'm blue in the face, but I'm not oblivious. (With aging comes wisdom and self-awareness.) These forces make successfully reimagining the workplace a herculean task. Many, if not most, business leaders will opt for an easier way out.

Regardless of which path you take, be thoughtful and deliberate. Constantly vacillating will only irk your employees, investors, shareholders, and partners. Pick a lane but, at the same time, admit when you're wrong. Your organization, department, and team won't always stick the landing. A little honesty goes a long way.

Explain to your constituents the changes you're making and why you're making them. And for heaven's sake, don't tell your employees that you've future-proofed your workplace or strategy. A change or idea that seems reasonable in 2023 might not seem so effective in 2025.

Colliding Forces and Limitless Possibilities

So much is unknown. How will *any* of these forces play out in isolation? How will one collide with others?

No can say with certainty. If someone claims otherwise, run.

Forces will collide in manifold and fascinating ways. Here are two of them.

First, how will generative AI affect employee empowerment and dispersed workforces? Will ChatGPT and its ilk swing the pendulum back to employers? Will employees swallow their pride and grudgingly return to the office five days per week? Will managers use generative AI to freeze employee wages and even reduce headcount? If done on a large scale, will that tame inflation?

Second and less abstractly, consider generative AI and immersive technologies. What will happen when these two powerful, ascending forces collide?

Joshua Browder has been thinking about this question for years. The CEO and founder of New York startup DoNotPay purports to offer top-tier legal advice at a fraction of the cost of hiring lawyers. The company's secret sauce consists of high-tech smart glasses that "record court proceedings and dictate responses into the defendant's ear from a small speaker."[29] Who needs a pricey lawyer to contest traffic tickets in court? Why not get all the taste with only a quarter of the calories?

There's just one problem: not everyone is on board. As Browder told NPR in January 2023, "Multiple state bars have threatened us. One even said a referral to the district attorney's office and prosecution and prison time would be possible."

Will technology ultimately replace lawyers who argue in front of judges? Again, no one knows. It may be unlikely, but it's *more* likely now than a decade ago.

We do know one thing with absolute certainty, however: the nine forces will continue to expand, morph, and collide with each other in unforeseen ways. As we've seen throughout this book, their effects on the workplace have *already* been profound. We ain't seen nothin' yet.

Equipped with that information, what are you going to do?

And that, in a nutshell, is the $64,000 question facing business leaders today.

Let me know if I can help you answer it.

Key Points

- When confronted with disruptive forces, newspapers generally kept their heads in the sand until it was too late. Plenty didn't survive.
- Nine powerful forces are driving a similar metamorphosis in the workplace.
- When faced with existential threats, Best Buy and Circuit City employed vastly different approaches. Only one of them is still standing.
- In response to the nine forces, senior leaders can opt for one of six approaches. Hope is not one of them.

THANK-YOU

"To defend what you've written is a sign that you are alive."

—WILLIAM ZINSSER

Thank you for buying *The Nine*. I hope that you've enjoyed the preceding pages. Ideally, you've found this book informative, and it has made you think. In some way, it has helped.

If that's true, then perhaps you're willing to help me.

Doing each of these things is helpful:

- Writing a book review on Amazon, bn.com, GoodReads, or your blog. The more honest, the better.
- Mentioning this book on Facebook, Reddit, Twitter, Quora, LinkedIn, and other sites you frequent.
- Recommending it to anyone who might find it interesting.
- Giving this book as a gift.
- Checking out my other titles, especially the previous three in this series.

I write books for several reasons. First, that's just what a writer does. Second, I believe I have something meaningful to say about an important topic. Third, I like writing, editing, crafting a cover, and all the other pieces that go into the puzzle of writing a good book. To paraphrase the title of an album by Geddy Lee, it's my favorite headache.

Fourth, although Kindles and iPads are downright cool, I enjoy holding a physical copy of one of my books. In our digital world, creating something tangible from scratch is glorious. I also find writing to be incredibly cathartic. Finally, new books open professional doors for me.

At the same time, producing quality text is no small feat. Every additional copy sold helps make the next one possible.

Phil Simon
www.philsimon.com
April 3, 2023

ACKNOWLEDGMENTS

For making this book happen: Luke Fletcher, Karen Davis, Jessica Angerstein, Vinnie Kinsella, Jonathan Yen, and Johnna VanHoose Dinse.

For their contributions: Sumithra Jagannath, Ken Weil, Martin Cavas, Karina Mikhli, and Jesse Fu.

A tip of the hat to the people who keep me grounded and listen to my rants: Dalton Cervo, Rob Hornyak, Hina Arora, Daniel Teachey, Eric Johnson, Emily Freeman, Chris Olsen, Steve Katz, Bruce Webster, Michael Viola, Joe Mirza, Dave Sandberg, Chris McGee, Scott Berkun, Jeff Pelletier, Josh Bernoff, Karin Reed, Martin Traub-Warner, Andrew Botwin, Moneet Singh, John Andrewski, Jimmy Jacobson, Rob Metting, Prescott Perez-Fox, Monica Meehan, Jason Horowitz, Marc Paolella, Peter and Hope Simon, Adom Asadourian, Helen Thompson, Kevin Daly, Sarah Garcia, Jason Conigliari, J. R. Camilon, Mark Pardy, Dustin Schott, Daniel Green, Matt Wagner, Michelle Gitlitz, Brian and Heather Morgan, Laurie Feuerstein, Autumn Torres (the world's best trainer), and especially my consigliere, Alan Simon.

Nietzsche once said, "Without music, life would be a mistake." He wasn't wrong.

For decades of incredible music, thank you to the members of Rush (Geddy, Alex, and Neil) and Marillion (h, Steve, Ian, Mark, and Pete). Your songs continue to inspire millions of discerning fans. I'm proud to call myself one of them.

Vince Gilligan, Peter Gould, Bryan Cranston, Aaron Paul, Dean Norris, Anna Gunn, Bob Odenkirk, Betsy Brandt, Jonathan Banks, Giancarlo Esposito, R J Mitte, Michael Mando, Rhea Seehorn, Michael McKean, Patrick Fabian, Tony Dalton, and the rest of the *Breaking Bad* and *Better Call Saul* teams have inspired me to do great work. Thank you for an epic fourteen-year run.

Finally, to my family: thank you.

ABOUT THE AUTHOR

Phil Simon is the world's leading independent expert on workplace collaboration and technology. He has penned many books, three of which have won awards. His prior text is *Low-Code/No-Code: Citizen Developers and the Surprising Future of Business Applications.* He helps organizations communicate, collaborate, and use technology better. *Harvard Business Review, MIT Sloan Management Review, Wired,* NBC, CNBC, *Bloomberg Businessweek,* and the *New York Times* have featured his contributions.

He also hosts the podcast *Conversations About Collaboration.* Simon holds degrees from Carnegie Mellon and Cornell University.

Thalacker Photography

BIBLIOGRAPHY

Alter, Adam. *Irresistible: The Rise of Addictive Technology and the Business of Keeping Us Hooked*. New York: Random House, 2017.

Asinof, Eliot. *Eight Men Out: The Black Sox and the 1919 World Series*. Bronx, New York: Ishi Press International, 2000.

Bailenson, Jeremy. *Experience on Demand: What Virtual Reality Is, How It Works, and What It Can Do*. New York: W. W. Norton, 2018.

Ball, Matthew. *The Metaverse: And How It Will Revolutionize Everything*. New York: Liveright Publishing Corp., 2022.

Bergen, Mark. *Like, Comment, Subscribe: Inside YouTube's Chaotic Rise to World Domination*. New York: Viking, 2022.

Bryar, Colin, and Bill Carr. *Working Backwards: Insights, Stories, and Secrets from Inside Amazon*. New York: St Martin's Press, 2021.

Burlingham, Bo. *Small Giants: Companies That Choose to Be Great Instead of Big*. New York: Portfolio, 2007.

Casey, Michael, and Paul Vigna. *The Truth Machine: The Blockchain and the Future of Everything*. New York: Picador, 2019.

Childress, Herb. *The Adjunct Underclass: How America's Colleges Betrayed Their Faculty, Their Students, and Their Mission*. Chicago: The University of Chicago Press, 2019.

Clear, James. *Atomic Habits: An Easy & Proven Way to Build Good Habits & Break Bad Ones*. New York: Penguin, 2019.

Elliott, Brian, Sheela Subramanian, and Helen Kupp. *How the Future Works: Leading Flexible Teams to Do the Best Work of Their Lives*. Hoboken, New Jersey: Wiley, 2022.

Galloway, Scott. *Adrift: America in 100 Charts*. New York: Random House, 2022.

Gladwell, Malcolm. *Outliers: The Story of Success*. New York: Little, Brown and Company, 2009.

Hammer, Michael, and James Champy. *Reengineering the Corporation: A Manifesto for Business Revolution*. New York: Collins Business Essentials, 1993.

Isaac, Mike. *Super Pumped: The Battle for Uber*. New York: W. W. Norton, 2019.

Levitt, Stephen J., and Steven D. Dubner. *Freakonomics: A Rogue Economist Explores the Hidden Side of Everything*. New York: William Morrow, 2005.

Lewis, Michael. *Moneyball: The Art of Winning an Unfair Game*. New York: W. W. Norton, 2003.

Miller, Chris. *Chip War: The Fight for the World's Most Critical Technology*. New York: Simon and Schuster, 2022.

Mims, Christopher. *Arriving Today: From Factory to Front Door— Why Everything Has Changed about How and What We Buy*. New York: HarperBusiness, 2021.

Muller, Jerry. *The Tyranny of Metrics*. Princeton, New Jersey: Princeton University Press, 2019.

Nilles, Jack. *The Telecommunications-Transportation Tradeoff: Options for Tomorrow*. Malabar, Florida: Krieger Publishing, 1976.

Norberg, Johan. *Progress: Ten Reasons to Look Forward to the Future*. London: Oneworld, 2018.

O'Neil, Cathy. *Weapons of Math Destruction: How Big Data Increases Inequality and Threatens Democracy*. London: Penguin Books, 2016.

Roose, Kevin. *Futureproof: 9 Rules for Humans in the Age of Automation*. New York: Random House, 2022.

Rose, David. *SuperSight: What Augmented Reality Means for Our Lives, Our Work, and the Way We Imagine the Future*. Dallas, Texas: BenBella Books, 2021.

Schwab, Klaus. *The Fourth Industrial Revolution*. London: Penguin Random House, 2016.

Stewart, Matthew. *The Management Myth: Why the Experts Keep Getting It Wrong*. New York: W. W. Norton, 2009.

Stolzoff, Simone. *The Good Enough Job: Reclaiming Life from Work*. London: Portfolio, 2023.

Taylor, Frederick Winslow. *The Principles of Scientific Management*. Harper & Brothers, 1911.

Ton, Zeynep. *The Good Jobs Strategy: How the Smartest Companies Invest in Employees to Lower Costs and Boost Profits*. Brighton, Massachusetts: Harvard Business Press, 2019.

Wolf, Ben. *Fractional Leadership: Landing Executive Talent You Thought Was out of Reach*. Houndstooth Press, 2021.

Zirin, Dave. *Bad Sports: How Owners Are Ruining the Games We Love*. New York: Simon and Schuster, 2010.

INDEX

ENDNOTES

CHAPTER 1

1. Lawrence Mishel, Elise Gould, and Josh Bivens. "Wage Stagnation in Nine Charts." Economic Policy Institute. January 6, 2015. https://tinyurl.com/y6hkxmvp.

2. Richard Henderson. "Stock Bulls Get Fresh Reason to Fret as Restive Workers Walk Out." Bloomberg.com. December 27, 2022. https://tinyurl.com/2ovu6gfs.

3. Lisa Marie Segarra. "More than 20,000 Google Employees Participated in Walkout over Sexual Harassment Policy." *Fortune.* November 3, 2018. https://tinyurl.com/2qxmz52d.

4. Emily Sullivan and Laurel Wamsley. "Google Employees Walk out to Protest Company's Treatment of Women." NPR. November 1, 2018. https://tinyurl.com/y8ajp7ac.

5. Daisuke Wakabayashi and Katie Benner. "How Google Protected Andy Rubin, the 'Father of Android.'" *New York Times.* October 25, 2018. https://tinyurl.com/yce7of9a.

6. Johana Bhuiyan. "The Google Walkout: What Protesters Demanded and What They Got." *Los Angeles Times.* November 6, 2019. https://tinyurl.com/2hm99kqf.

7. Thomas Mirmotahari. "11 Awesome Google Benefits and Perks for Employees." www.perkupapp.com. January 6, 2022. https://tinyurl.com/2f5j3l4j.

8. Lauren Feiner. "Google CEO on Employee Walkouts: 'Moments Like This Show That We Didn't Always Get It Right.'" CNBC. November 1, 2018. https://tinyurl.com/ycl8hvek.

9. "About—Kickstarter." Kickstarter. https://tinyurl.com/2j2srsvf.

10. Yancey Strickler, Perry Chen, and Charles Adler. "Kickstarter Is Now a Benefit Corporation." Kickstarter. September 21, 2015. https://tinyurl.com/qd8gr69.

11. "B Corp Certification Demonstrates a Company's Entire Social and Environmental Impact." B Corporation. https://tinyurl.com/29jmd4k7.

12. "Kickstarter Reviews." Glassdoor. https://tinyurl.com/2gkftt45.

13. Ben Ferrari. "Always Punch Nazis." Kickstarter. March 26, 2021. https://tinyurl.com/2pgegcfk.

14. Bryce Covert. "How Kickstarter Employees Formed a Union." *Wired.* May 27, 2020. https://tinyurl.com/2jz3gm26.

15. "Kickstarter Accused of Union-Busting after Firing Workers." BBC. September 13, 2019, sec. US & Canada. https://tinyurl.com/2k2yny9u.

16. Bryce Covert. "How Kickstarter Employees Formed a Union." *Wired.* May 27, 2020. https://tinyurl.com/2jz3gm26.

17. Justin McCarthy. "U.S. Approval of Labor Unions at Highest Point Since 1965." Gallup.com. August 30, 2022. https://tinyurl.com/2o6zkt94.

18. Lindsay Ellis and Ray Smith. "Your Coworkers Are Less Ambitious; Bosses Adjust to the New Order." *Wall Street Journal.* December 31, 2022. https://tinyurl.com/2ksy5qas.

19. Jack Zenger and Joseph Folkman. "Quiet Quitting Is about Bad Bosses, Not Bad Employees." *Harvard Business Review.* August 31, 2022. https://tinyurl.com/2fyba2dq.

20. "Young Workers Are Ambitious about Work Now—So They Can Retire Early." Qualtrics. January 4, 2023. https://tinyurl.com/2zy7nck5.

21. "Table 1. Median Years of Tenure with Current Employer for Employed Wage and Salary Workers by Age and Sex, Selected Years, 2010–2020." U.S. Bureau of Labor Statistics. January 15, 2022. https://tinyurl.com/2orfgely.

22. "What Is China's 996 Work Culture That Has Claimed Another Techie's Life: All You Need to Know about It." First Post. February 10, 2022. https://tinyurl.com/2p3we8me.

23. Paul Rubenstein. "Did Your Employee Ghost You? Here's Why." *Entrepreneur.* March 17, 2022. https://tinyurl.com/2pgmh84q.

24. "The Hot Job Market Is Cooling Off. Why Are New Hires Still Ghosting Employers?" *Fast Company.* July 22, 2022. https://tinyurl.com/2fzap6by.

25. "U.S. Surgeon General Releases New Framework for Mental Health & Well-Being in the Workplace." HHS.gov. October 20, 2022. https://tinyurl.com/2bv8tk3x.

26. "2023 Leave of Absence Forecast Survey Results." AbsenceSoft. January 17, 2023. https://tinyurl.com/2bkpjoqp.

27. "The Great Resignation Update: Limeade Employee Care Report." Limeade. September 29, 2021. https://tinyurl.com/2yh5qka7.

28. Tess McClure. "Jacinda Ardern Resigns as Prime Minister of New Zealand." *The Guardian.* January 19, 2023. https://tinyurl.com/2eqfm4y4.

29. Stephanie Saul. "At N.Y.U., Students Were Failing Organic Chemistry. Who Was to Blame?" *New York Times.* October 3, 2022, sec. U.S. https://tinyurl.com/2o2k6vo3.

30. Stephanie Saul. "At N.Y.U., Students Were Failing Organic Chemistry. Who Was to Blame?" *New York Times.* October 3, 2022, sec. U.S. https://tinyurl.com/2o2k6vo3.

31. Jessica Dickler. "Share of Americans Living Paycheck to Paycheck Rises to 63%— Here's How to Get Your Finances Back on Track." CNBC. December 15, 2020. https://tinyurl.com/2jc7ths6.

32. Cat Zakrzewski. "The Technology 202: State Unemployment Websites Are Crashing Amid Record Number of Claims." *Washington Post.* April 2, 2020. https://tinyurl.com/26fh82y5.

33. "COVID-19 Unemployment Benefits Slowed Return to Work." NBER. February 1, 2022. https://tinyurl.com/2996jhpy.

34. Jeff Borzello. "Texas Fires Beard Amid Domestic Violence Charge." ESPN.com. January 5, 2023. https://tinyurl.com/2ldvrqck.

35. Ken Belson and Katherine Rosman. "Congress Says Dan Snyder and the N.F.L. Impeded Sexual Harassment Investigation." *New York Times.* December 8, 2022, sec. Sports. https://tinyurl.com/2osarxwd.

36. Marc Raimondi. "Report: WWE's McMahon Paid $12M to 4 Women." ESPN.com. July 8, 2022. https://tinyurl.com/2pebum5j.

37. Jack Ewing. "Founder of Electric Truck Maker Is Convicted of Fraud." *New York Times.* October 14, 2022, sec. Business. https://tinyurl.com/2onbdm4d.

38. Ryan Faughnder. "Streaming Milestone: Global Subscriptions Passed 1 Billion Last Year." *Los Angeles Times.* March 18, 2021. https://tinyurl.com/2hp4vyrd.

39. "Netflix Is Serious About Password Sharing Crackdown." Nerdist. December 27, 2022. https://tinyurl.com/2gywvnsj.

40. "Americans Reading Fewer Books Than in Past." Gallup. January 10, 2022. https://tinyurl.com/2ksg32sl.

41. Kevin Roose. "Elon Musk, Management Guru?" *New York Times*. December 16, 2022, sec. Technology. https://tinyurl.com/2k95hwjg.

42. Kate Conger, Ryan Mac, and Mike Isaac. "What's Gone at Twitter? A Data Center, Janitors, Some Toilet Paper." *New York Times*. December 29, 2022, sec. Technology. https://tinyurl.com/2z7gguuy.

43. Mia Sato. "Hundreds of Employees Say No to Being Part of Elon Musk's 'Extremely Hardcore' Twitter." The Verge. November 17, 2022. https://tinyurl.com/2jd6hnwo.

44. Stephen Miller. "Employee Resource Groups Create a Sense of Belonging, Foster Engagement." SHRM. June 12, 2022. https://tinyurl.com/2qlnnzqd.

45. Layoffs.fyi. "Tech Layoff Tracker and Startup Layoff Lists." https://layoffs.fyi.

46. Jordan Novet. "Microsoft Is Laying Off 10,000 Employees." CNBC. January 18, 2023. https://tinyurl.com/2nadt2ho.

47. Chip Cutter and Theo Francis. "The Bosses Are Back in Charge." *Wall Street Journal*. February 2, 2023. https://tinyurl.com/2dosgwne.

48. "https://Tinyurl.com/Y9s87339." Bureau of Labor Statistics. November 20, 2022.

49. "Employment Situation Frequently Asked Questions." US Bureau of Labor Statistics. https://tinyurl.com/2pkftzjo.

50. Megan Cerullo. "Why Have So Many American Men Given Up on Work?" CBS News. December 9, 2022. https://tinyurl.com/2fm2n7hw.

51. Sarah O'Connor. "Young Men Are Slipping Quietly Through the Economy's Cracks." *Financial Times*. June 28, 2022. https://tinyurl.com/2ofxg7rt.

52. "Reimagining the Workforce for the Digital Age: An RSM and US Chamber Discussion." The Real Economy Blog. February 18, 2022. https://tinyurl.com/2ywcvrkr.

53. "Employment Projections—2021." Bureau of Labor Statistics. September 8, 2022. https://tinyurl.com/28lngvqp.

54. Patrick Coate. "Economic Outlook for Q3 2022." Quarterly Economics Briefing. November 14, 2022. https://tinyurl.com/26evv7dg.

55. "Job Openings and Labor Turnover Survey Home Page." Bureau of Labor Statistics. January 25, 2023. https://www.bls.gov/jlt.

56. Tara Watson. "The Decline in U.S. Net Migration" Econofact.org. March 7, 2022. https://tinyurl.com/242etzde.

57. Jeffrey S. Passel and D'Vera Cohn. "After Declining Early in the COVID-19 Outbreak, Immigrant Naturalizations in the U.S. Are Rising Again." Pew Research Center. December 1, 2022. https://tinyurl.com/2h5pzeda.

58. "The Long-Term Decline in Fertility—and What It Means for State Budgets." Pew Research. December 5, 2022. https://tinyurl.com/2e4wuryq.

59. Yamamoto Saori. "Japan's Plummeting Birth Rate Prompts Calls for Action." NHK WORLD. December 15, 2022. https://tinyurl.com/27ug5xvt.

60. "France's High Fertility Rate Has Begun to Slide." *The Economist*. February 17, 2018. https://tinyurl.com/22gr5mc2.

61. Jessica Dickler. "Student Loan Debt Is a Hurdle for Many Would-Be Mothers." CNBC. May 22, 2018. https://tinyurl.com/y9ceqv34.

62. "Side Hustles, Extra Shifts, or a New Job—Inflation Forcing Workers to Raise Their Incomes." *Qualtrics.* October 17, 2022. https://tinyurl.com/2e6t2xq9.

63. Maggie Davis. "Survey: Side Hustlers on the Rise." LendingTree. December 5, 2022. https://tinyurl.com/2fvj3ev5.

64. Will Kenton. "Non-Compete Agreements: What You Need to Know." Investopedia. June 29, 2021. https://tinyurl.com/2je8ffhu.

65. "The Basics of Non-Compete Agreements." Thomson Reuters. March 11, 2022. https://tinyurl.com/2eggp3ln.

66. "FTC Proposes Rule to Ban Noncompete Clauses, Which Hurt Workers and Harm Competition." Federal Trade Commission. January 4, 2023. https://tinyurl.com/2nypupex.

67. Lina M. Khan. "Lina Khan: Noncompetes Depress Wages and Kill Innovation." *New York Times.* January 9, 2023, sec. Opinion. https://tinyurl.com/2ealtoum.

CHAPTER 2

1. Mark Gurman. "Apple Pays Another Round of Rare $200,000 Bonuses to Some Staff." Bloomberg.com. March 25, 2022. https://tinyurl.com/2gml9ggz.

2. Dan Levine. "Steve Jobs Told Google to Stop Poaching Workers." Reuters. January 27, 2012, sec. Technology News. https://tinyurl.com/2ml5ntd5.

3. Ian Goodfellow. "LinkedIn Profile." LinkedIn. https://tinyurl.com/2e48q96j.

4. Kelly Main. "Apple's $5 Billion Office Complex Offers an Important Lesson About Employee Well-Being." Inc.com. June 20, 2022. https://tinyurl.com/2ens45wc.

5. "2022 End-of-Year Hot Jobs Report." Payscale. December 13, 2022. https://tinyurl.com/2eaegt5u.

6. Dennis Consorte. "1 in 4 Remote Workers Refuse In-Office Mandate." Reli Exchange. November 8, 2022. https://tinyurl.com/2grf5twq.

7. Jacques Buffett. "Return to Office or Stay Remote? What Workers Want in 2022." Zety. October 10, 2022. https://tinyurl.com/2lznpnx8.

8. Abha Bhattarai. "The Great Mismatch: Remote Jobs Are in Demand, but Positions Are Drying Up." *Washington Post.* November 7, 2022. https://tinyurl.com/2lrgj2bm.

9. "Executives Feel the Strain of Leading in the 'New Normal.'" Future Forum. October 10, 2022. https://tinyurl.com/28d5463v.

10. Dean Mirshahi. "Over 300 Virginia State Employees Resign in Wake of Gov. Youngkin's Telework Policy." WRIC ABC 8 News. July 8, 2022. https://tinyurl.com/2nkk68y8.

11. "Over 800 WhiteHat Jr Employees Resign After Being Asked to Return to Office: Report." CNBC. May 11, 2022. https://tinyurl.com/2lmj9tzw.

12. "SHRM Research Reveals Negative Perceptions of Remote Work." SHRM. July 26, 2021. https://tinyurl.com/yayledlu.

13. "Employers' Post-COVID Business Strategy and the Race for Talent." Northeastern University. https://tinyurl.com/2mmm8muo.

14. Jennifer Liu. "Bosses Are Increasing RTO Requirements, but Experts Say It Won't Stick: 'We're at an Inflection Point.'" CNBC. January 20, 2023. https://tinyurl.com/2z8oyn84.

15. C. G. Aksoy et al. "Time Savings When Working From Home." NBER. https://www.nber.org/papers/w30866. January 23, 2023.

16. Jo Constantz. "Will Remote Work Continue in 2023?" Bloomberg.com. January 3, 2023. https://tinyurl.com/2ksjscgr.
17. Sara Korolevich. "The State of Remote Work in 2021 Survey." GoodHire. August 24, 2021. https://tinyurl.com/2g7r5xgf.
18. Alexandra Samuel and Terri Griffith. "Six Signs Your Hybrid Workplace Plan Isn't Working." *Wall Street Journal.* December 13, 2022. https://tinyurl.com/2faqu9df.
19. "40+ Stats for Companies to Keep in Mind for 2021." Glassdoor for Employers. July 1, 2021. https://tinyurl.com/2f9shcbq.
20. Arian Campo-Flores et al. "The Pandemic Changed Where Americans Live." *Wall Street Journal.* April 27, 2021, sec. US. https://tinyurl.com/2q6fl7bx.
21. "How Technology Is Redrawing the Boundaries of the Firm." *The Economist.* January 8, 2023. https://tinyurl.com/2zd3kf6b.
22. Gleb Tsipursky. "What Is Proximity Bias and How Can Managers Prevent It?" *Harvard Business Review.* October 4, 2022. https://tinyurl.com/2ov2k8hg.
23. "SHRM Research Reveals Negative Perceptions of Remote Work." Society for Human Resource Management. July 26, 2021. https://tinyurl.com/yayledlu.
24. Lisa Ardill. "Dropbox in Dublin Going 'Virtual First' With Permanent Remote Working Plan." Silicon Republic. October 14, 2020. https://tinyurl.com/2k6n6nrd.
25. "Form 10-Q for Dropbox, Inc." November 4, 2022. Dropbox. https://tinyurl.com/2p7yynvu.
26. Bruce Horovitz. "Dropbox Tossed Out the Workplace Rulebook." *Time.* September 12, 2022. https://tinyurl.com/2gytknaj.
27. Andrew Cave. "Mark Dixon: The Briton Who Wants to Build a New Google." *The Telegraph.* April 25, 2009. https://tinyurl.com/2qjhaen9.
28. Dror Poleg. "The Future of Offices When Workers Have a Choice." *New York Times.* January 4, 2021, sec. The Upshot. https://tinyurl.com/y7d3or9h.
29. Morgan Greenwald. "Starbucks Debuts 'Innovative' Coworking Concept at All-New Store: 'a New Place to Live.'" Yahoo. August 18, 2020. https://tinyurl.com/2q6q2ky5.
30. Ed Berthiaume. "Jack Nilles Tried to Ignite a Work-From-Home Trend 48 Years Ago. It's Finally Here." Lawrence University." August 17, 2020. https://tinyurl.com/2ohostsx.
31. Jack Riewe. "Designers Behind Google and Microsoft's Headquarters Imagine What Satellite Offices Could Look Like for Companies Eager to Return to a Safe, Collaborative Workplace." Insider. January 21, 2021. https://tinyurl.com/2n94jl73.
32. Bryan Robinson. "'Hub-And-Spoke': The New Office Model of the Future, Expert Says." *Forbes.* June 9, 2021. https://tinyurl.com/2oxh9hxj.

CHAPTER 3

1. Jon Hilsenrath and Rachel Wolfe. "Inflation Takes Biggest Bite From Middle-Income Households." *Wall Street Journal.* December 28, 2022. https://tinyurl.com/2nye9ofx.
2. "Current US Inflation Rates: 2000–2022." US Inflation Calculator. https://tinyurl.com/y7anknow.
3. "Why Inflation Looks Likely to Stay Above the Pre-Pandemic Norm." *The Economist.* July 26, 2022. https://tinyurl.com/26258dsw.

4. "Temporary Layoffs Remain High Following Unprecedented Surge in Early 2020." U.S. Bureau of Labor Statistics. February 10, 2021. https://tinyurl.com/y4blzbel.

5. "Advance Child Tax Credit and Economic Impact Payments—Stimulus Checks." USAGov. https://tinyurl.com/2gaffo3r.

6. David J. Lynch. "Inflation Has Fed Critics Pointing to Spike in Money Supply." *Washington Post.* February 6, 2022. https://tinyurl.com/yc9ek9qc.

7. Catherine Choi. "Do Americans Save Money Like Other Countries?" Finder.com. October 3, 2019. https://tinyurl.com/2jokpxr3.

8. Vivian Yee and James Glanz. "How One of the World's Biggest Ships Jammed the Suez Canal." *New York Times.* July 17, 2021, sec. World. https://tinyurl.com/yhag5l5z.

9. Martin Placek. "Topic: Container Freight Rates." Statista. July 12, 2012. https://tinyurl.com/2h2zjk82.

10. Stephen Nellis and David Shepardson. "Taiwan's TSMC to Build Arizona Chip Plant as U.S.-China Tech Rivalry Escalates." Reuters. May 14, 2020, sec. Technology News. https://tinyurl.com/2fzl8xwo.

11. Sam Shead. "Samsung Plans to Build a $17 Billion Chip Plant in Texas." CNBC. November 24, 2021. https://tinyurl.com/2la76hwp.

12. Jeanne Whalen. "Biden's Visit Shows High Stakes of $20 Billion Ohio Chip Factory." *Washington Post.* September 10, 2022. https://tinyurl.com/2m3hu3ay.

13. Arjun Kharpal. "Apple Begins Making the iPhone 14 in India, Marking a Big Shift in Its Manufacturing Strategy." CNBC. September 26, 2022. https://tinyurl.com/2kpyrcz7.

14. T. H. Tulchinsky (2018). "John Snow, Cholera, the Broad Street Pump; Waterborne Diseases Then and Now." Case Studies in Public Health, 77–99. https://doi.org/10.1016/B978-0-12-804571-8.00017-2.

15. "Kodak." Kodak. https://www.kodak.com/en.

16. Jennifer Williams-Alvarez. "Companies Cut Orders, Build Up Inventory as Supply Disruptions Continue." *Wall Street Journal.* May 20, 2022, sec. C Suite. https://tinyurl.com/2q5dprtp.

17. "TimesMachine." *New York Times.* March 7, 1973. https://tinyurl.com/2j23up52.

18. Justin Lahart. "The Fed's Fear of a Wage-Price Spiral Might Soon Abate." *Wall Street Journal.* January 6, 2023. https://tinyurl.com/2nna6mld.

19. Brett Holzhauer. "Airline Ticket Prices Are Up 25%, Outpacing Inflation—Here Are the Ways You Can Still Save." CNBC. May 14, 2022. https://tinyurl.com/2j9ulhxm.

20. "Consumer Checkpoint: Still Smiling." Bank of America Institute. May 5, 2022. https://tinyurl.com/2pybyouq.

21. Katherine Schaeffer. "Key Facts About Housing Affordability in the U.S." Pew Research Center. March 23, 2022. https://tinyurl.com/y6d6znuu.

22. Emily Peck. "Why Rents Are Soaring Pretty Much Everywhere in the U.S." Axios. August 16, 2022. https://tinyurl.com/2gblwhpk.

23. Richard Fry, Jeffrey S. Passel, and D'Vera Cohn. "A Majority of Young Adults in the U.S. Live With Their Parents for the First Time Since the Great Depression." Pew Research Center. September 4, 2020. https://tinyurl.com/y42894ps.

24. Jennifer Liu. "All the U.S. States, Cities and Counties Where Companies Have to Share Salary Ranges with Workers." CNBC. January 3, 2023. https://tinyurl.com/2nvafnsk.

25. Jordan Jantz. "Pay Transparency Laws: What HR Pros Need to Know." June 20, 2022. https://tinyurl.com/2hgdhz7u.
26. Matthew Boyle. "Work Shift: Pay Transparency's Unintended Consequences." Bloomberg.com. November 8, 2022. https://tinyurl.com/2qprlcbs.
27. "Compa-Ratio." SHRM. July 15, 2021. https://tinyurl.com/2q7kybwl.

CHAPTER 4

1. Alice Gibbs. "Welcome to the First Ever McDonald's Where You're Served by Robots—in Texas." *Newsweek.* December 22, 2022. https://tinyurl.com/2o5r9tg8.
2. James Feigenbaum and Daniel P. Gross. "Automation and the Fate of Young Workers: Evidence From Telephone Operation in the Early 20th Century." Cato.org. 2023. https://tinyurl.com/2qlao69m.
3. A. W. Geiger. "How Americans See Automation and the Workplace in 7 Charts." Pew Research Center. April 8, 2019. https://tinyurl.com/y2hnktyl.
4. Carl Benedikt Frey and Michael A. Osborne. 2013. "The Future of Employment: How Susceptible Are Jobs to Computerisation?" *Technological Forecasting and Social Change* 114 (1): 254–80. https://doi.org/10.1016/j.techfore.2016.08.019.
5. "The Imperatives for Success with Automation Technologies." McKinsey & Company. August 25, 2020. https://tinyurl.com/2quym3c8.
6. "ISO 9407:2019: Footware Sizing—Mondopoint System of Sizing and Marking." ISO. June 15, 2019. https://bit.ly/3PRvfdG.
7. Clem. "A Self-Serve Popcorn Machine Is the Biggest Game Changer in Movie Theater History Since the Invention of the Projector." December 30, 2021. https://tinyurl.com/2hrenk89.
8. Scott Beyer. "Autonomous Trucks Are Coming Sooner Than You Think." Catalyst. December 30, 2022. https://tinyurl.com/2zduvo7r.
9. Davey Alba and Kurt Wagner. "Twitter Cuts More Staff Overseeing Global Content Moderation." Bloomberg.com. January 7, 2023. https://tinyurl.com/2q76eova.
10. Chloe Aiello. 2018. "Uber's Loss Jumped 61 Percent to $4.5 Billion in 2017." CNBC. February 14, 2018. https://tinyurl.com/y722axw2.
11. Katie Roof. "SoftBank's Big Investment in Uber Comes to a Close." TechCrunch. December 28, 2017. https://tinyurl.com/2jbc7eym.
12. "Uber Maintains Global Infrastructure Built on UiPath RPA." UiPath. December 6, 2021. https://tinyurl.com/2em6vkqv.
13. "Leveraging Intelligent Process Automation: 1300% ROI Delivers Increased CSAT and $7m in New Revenue Streams." Automation Anywhere. March 4, 2021. https://tinyurl.com/2qmmnl8s.
14. "KeyBank Completes Nine Years of Work in Just Two Weeks With Intelligent Automation." Automation Anywhere. March 4, 2021. https://tinyurl.com/273a9ndl.
15. "NHS Improves Workforce Processes with RPA." Automation Anywhere. April 12, 2021. https://tinyurl.com/2ex59cwe.
16. Laurence Goasduff. "Gartner Says Worldwide RPA Software Spending to Reach $2.9 Billion in 2022." Gartner. August 1, 2022. https://tinyurl.com/2p6qe933.
17. "The RPA Market Will Grow to $22 Billion by 2025." Forrester. February 22, 2022. https://tinyurl.com/2enc569h.

18. Happy Sharer. "Exploring Who Invented Regression Testing: An Interview with the Inventor, a History and Its Impact." The Enlightened Mindset. January 23, 2023. https://tinyurl.com/2fwo4y37.

19. "Stack Overflow Developer Survey 2022." Stack Overflow. June 22, 2022. https://tinyurl.com/2z642rfm.

20. Phil Simon. "How I Use Slack Inside of the Classroom." Blog. September 28, 2017. https://tinyurl.com/y3rgxl2v.

21. Jurica Dujmovic. "As Coronavirus Hits Hard, Amazon Starts Licensing Cashier-Free Technology to Retailers." MarketWatch. March 31, 2020. https://tinyurl.com/23o8we8t.

22. Barney Jopson. "The Bezos Doctrine of Ruthless Pragmatism." *Financial Times*. July 9, 2012. https://tinyurl.com/2dm9pph7.

23. Alex Kantrowitz. "How Amazon Automated Work and Put Its People to Better Use." *Harvard Business Review*. September 16, 2020. https://tinyurl.com/2md88nft.

24. Alex Kantrowitz. "How Amazon Uses AI to Automate Work in Its Corporate Headquarters." Big Technology. December 22, 2022. https://tinyurl.com/2kmstxd6.

25. Ryan Fan. "I Got a Job at an Amazon Warehouse Without Talking to a Single Human." Medium. July 16, 2020. https://tinyurl.com/y27nz4us.

26. Adam Putz. "M&A Flashback: Amazon Announces $775M Kiva Systems Acquisition." PitchBook. March 19, 2018. https://tinyurl.com/2fmqzrvb.

CHAPTER 5

1. Tiago Bianchi. "U.S. Mobile Search Share 2020." Statista. December 1, 2022. https://tinyurl.com/2gztudpj.

2. Daniel Ruby. "26+ iPhone User & Sales Statistics (Fresh Data 2022)." Demandsage. July 12, 2022. https://tinyurl.com/2nd4xcao.

3. "What Is Deep Learning? 3 Things You Need to Know." MathWorks. https://tinyurl.com/y2po4so6.

4. Derek Thompson. "Breakthroughs of the Year." *The Atlantic*. December 8, 2022. https://tinyurl.com/2kxt2v6e.

5. Cade Metz. "How Smart Are the Robots Getting?" *New York Times*. January 20, 2023, sec. Technology. https://tinyurl.com/2q3mhhkd.

6. Mira Murati. Twitter. December 5, 2022. https://tinyurl.com/2eomchzb.

7. Sam Altman. Twitter. December 10, 2022. https://tinyurl.com/2pgvoqtv.

8. Scott Galloway. "The Prof G Pod With Scott Galloway: The AI Hype Cycle—With Gary Marcus." Apple Podcasts. January 19, 2023. https://tinyurl.com/2jhzummm.

9. Noor Al-Sibai. "Facebook Takes Down AI That Churns Out Fake Academic Papers After Widespread Criticism." Futurism. November 20, 2022. https://tinyurl.com/2ojpsfpu.

10. Kevin Roose. "A Coming-Out Party for Generative A.I., Silicon Valley's New Craze." *New York Times*. October 21, 2022, sec. Technology. https://tinyurl.com/2d9qoyzb.

11. "A Sharp Increase in AI-Related Venture Capitalist Investments Could Transform Global Economies and Shape the Future of Artificial Intelligence." OECD.AI. https://oecd.ai/en/vc.

12. Sonya Huang and Pat Grady. "Generative AI: A Creative New World." Sequoia Capital US/Europe. September 19, 2022. https://tinyurl.com/2eo69gfq.

13. "Investors Seek to Profit from Groundbreaking 'Generative AI' Start-Ups." *Financial Times.* December 9, 2022. https://tinyurl.com/2gb3xphu.
14. CB Insights. "The Generative AI Landscape: Top Startups, Venture Capital Firms, and More." CB Insights Research. January 25, 2023. https://tinyurl.com/2jqp6m2u.
15. "CIO Vision 2025: Bridging the Gap between BI and AI." *MIT Technology Review.* September 20, 2022. https://tinyurl.com/2jp47nfp.
16. Kyle Wiggers. "AI Content Platform Jasper Raises $125M at a $1.5B Valuation." TechCrunch. October 18, 2022. https://tinyurl.com/2gppxehd.
17. Chris Metinko. "After a Lot of Hype, (Useful) AI May Finally Be Here." Crunchbase News. November 3, 2022. https://tinyurl.com/27xvutgl.
18. Sissi Cao. "OpenAI, the Company Behind ChatGPT, Is Valued at $29 Billion." *Observer.* January 6, 2023. https://tinyurl.com/2eu4bfjp.
19. "DALL·E: Creating Images from Text." OpenAI. January 5, 2021. https://tinyurl.com/y63nb7hy.
20. "DALL·E 2." OpenAI. https://tinyurl.com/yag57s39.
21. Kyle Wiggers. "While Anticipation Builds for GPT-4, OpenAI Quietly Releases GPT-3.5." *TechCrunch.* December 2, 2022. https://tinyurl.com/2ldp7dxn.
22. "Your AI Pair Programmer." GitHub. June 22, 2022. https://tinyurl.com/25v3cawy.
23. Dave Gershgorn. "GitHub and OpenAI Launch a New AI Tool That Generates Its Own Code." The Verge. June 29, 2021. https://tinyurl.com/yewga8a2.
24. Ivan Zhao. "Introducing Notion AI." Notion. November 16, 2022. https://tinyurl.com/2lcwt27f.
25. Canva. "Turn Imagination into Reality with Text to Image in Canva." November 10, 2022. https://tinyurl.com/2n6kdq9l.
26. Cameron Adams. "Introducing Magic Write in Canva Docs." December 7, 2022. https://tinyurl.com/2kun8gjz.
27. Edwin Khodabakchian. "Meet Leo, Your AI Research Assistant." Feedly Blog. January 18, 2020. https://tinyurl.com/2lyobwba.
28. Sam Schechner. "Microsoft Plans to Build OpenAI, ChatGPT Features into All Products." *Wall Street Journal.* January 17, 2023. https://tinyurl.com/2mdpghyo.
29. Nick Lomas. "How Much Do Caddies Make? You Might Be Surprised." Golf Span. September 5, 2022. https://tinyurl.com/2mucvu8h.
30. Robert Solow. "We'd Better Watch Out." *New York Times.* https://tinyurl.com/2unrduy.
31. "Total Factor Productivity at Constant National Prices for Italy." FRED. November 8, 2021. https://tinyurl.com/2fdgnwc7.
32. Eli Dourado. "Heretical Thoughts on AI." January 19, 2023. https://tinyurl.com/2k6aw639.
33. Amanda Silberling. "Lensa AI Climbs the App Store Charts as Its 'Magic Avatars' Go Viral." TechCrunch. December 1, 2022. https://tinyurl.com/2qxuf65k.
34. "ChatGPT: Grading Artificial Intelligence's Writing." YouTube. January 22, 2023. https://tinyurl.com/2gqwc28m.
35. Michael Casey. "ChatGPT Will Kill Search and Open a Path to Web3." CoinDesk. December 9, 2022. https://tinyurl.com/2gkkk5c9.

36. Megan Graham and Jennifer Elias. "How Google's $150 Billion Advertising Business Works." CNBC. May 18, 2021. https://tinyurl.com/yeonbq46.

37. Joanna Stern. "I Tried Microsoft's New AI-Powered Bing. Search Will Never Be the Same." *Wall Street Journal.* February 7, 2023. https://tinyurl.com/23dvp69b.

38. "Global Search Engine Desktop Market Share 2022." Statista. February 1, 2023. https://tinyurl.com/yaqqkea9.

39. Jennifer Elias. "Google Shows Off More of What Its ChatGPT Competitor Bard Can Do." CNBC. February 8, 2023. https://tinyurl.com/25tavjkg.

40. Stability AI. "Stable Diffusion Version 2." GitHub. January 18, 2023. https://tinyurl.com/2k5c78nb.

41. Samantha Cole. "This AI Tool Is Being Used to Make Freaky, Machine-Generated Porn." Vice. August 24, 2022. https://tinyurl.com/2jd4e2cm.

42. Barbara Ortutay. "Why the Anthony Bourdain Voice Cloning Creeps People Out." AP NEWS. July 17, 2021. https://tinyurl.com/yhktnbrt.

43. "What's the Deal with Using Disney Intellectual Property?" The Mouselets. January 18, 2019. https://tinyurl.com/2lgnlloo.

44. Morgan Sung. "Lensa, the AI Portrait App, Has Soared in Popularity. But Many Artists Question the Ethics of AI Art." NBC News. December 6, 2022. https://tinyurl.com/2ot6lzdn.

45. James Vincent. "AI Art Tools Stable Diffusion and Midjourney Targeted With Copyright Lawsuit." The Verge. January 16, 2023. https://tinyurl.com/2fok7myt.

46. James Vincent. "Getty Images Is Suing the Creators of AI Art Tool Stable Diffusion for Scraping Its Content." The Verge. January 17, 2023. https://tinyurl.com/2grtz6uo.

47. James Vincent. "The Scary Truth about AI Copyright Is Nobody Knows What Will Happen Next." The Verge. November 15, 2022. https://tinyurl.com/28lt8xoc.

48. Kyle Wiggers. "Google Created an AI That Can Generate Music From Text Descriptions, but Won't Release It." TechCrunch. January 27, 2023. https://tinyurl.com/2j3wz3du.

49. Kalley Huang. "Alarmed by A.I. Chatbots, Universities Start Revamping How They Teach." *New York Times.* January 16, 2023, sec. Technology. https://tinyurl.com/2k3z8vv7.

50. Ali Aliev. "Avatarify Python." GitHub. December 10, 2021. https://tinyurl.com/2pv3jdrw.

51. Sean Berry. "How You Can Fake Being on a Zoom Video Call." Videomaker. April 7, 2020. https://tinyurl.com/2hxbhmro.

52. Christopher Cox. "Elon Musk's Appetite for Destruction." *New York Times.* January 17, 2023, sec. Magazine. https://tinyurl.com/2fngy37l.

53. Dana Hull and Sean O'Kane. "Musk Oversaw Video That Exaggerated Tesla's Self-Driving Capabilities." Bloomberg. January 19, 2023. https://tinyurl.com/2zhgz782.

54. Frank Landymore. "CNET Is Quietly Publishing Entire Articles Generated by AI." Futurism. January 11, 2023. https://tinyurl.com/2zthmnzn.

55. Jon Christian. "CNET's Article-Writing AI Is Already Publishing Very Dumb Errors." Futurism. January 17, 2023. https://tinyurl.com/2zl8dtm7.

56. Ross Miller. "AP's 'Robot Journalists' Are Writing Their Own Stories Now." The Verge. January 29, 2015. https://tinyurl.com/2q8wvtg8.

57. Alexandra Bruell. "BuzzFeed to Use ChatGPT Creator OpenAI to Help Create Quizzes and Other Content." *Wall Street Journal.* January 26, 2023. https://tinyurl.com/2pjqtsda.

58. Nick Carr. "How Many Computers Does the World Need?" *The Guardian.* February 21, 2008. https://tinyurl.com/2jkavxhl.

59. Jayson Derrick. "Remember When Yahoo Turned Down $1 Million to Buy Google?" Yahoo. July 16, 2016. https://tinyurl.com/ybs7hbhb.

60. Bloomberg TV. Tweet. https://inyurl.com/2fszaggf." Twitter. December 9, 2022.

61. Alex Kantrowitz. "How Amazon Uses AI to Automate Work in Its Corporate Headquarters." www.linkedin.com. December 27, 2022. https://tinyurl.com/2eb76srp.

62. James Vincent. "OpenAI CEO Sam Altman on GPT-4: 'People Are Begging to Be Disappointed and They Will Be.'" The Verge. January 18, 2023. https://tinyurl.com/2kan8u2p.

63. Eli Dourado. "Heretical Thoughts on AI." January 19, 2023. https://tinyurl.com/2k6aw639.

CHAPTER 6

1. Gustavo Miller. "LinkedIn Post." LinkedIn. December 22, 2022. https://tinyurl.com/2htq33qe.

2. Gustavo Miller. "LinkedIn Post." LinkedIn. December 22, 2022. https://tinyurl.com/2htq33qe.

3. Imani Moise. "Laid-Off Workers Are Flooded with Fake Job Offers." *Wall Street Journal.* January 11, 2022. https://tinyurl.com/2eoh2sq7.

4. "Yahoo Claims 'Cause' in CEO Scott Thompson Departure (Report)." *Hollywood Reporter.* May 14, 2012. https://tinyurl.com/2fja6v4y.

5. Ian Leonard. "Psychiatrist Zholia Alemi Accused of Faking Medical Degree." *New York Post.* January 11, 2023. https://tinyurl.com/2e4fcgwp.

6. BusinessWire. "JPMorgan Chase Acquires Frank, the Leading College Financial Planning Platform for Students." www.businesswire.com. September 21, 2021. https://tinyurl.com/2qtqtvd8.

7. BusinessWire. "JPMorgan Chase Acquires Frank, the Leading College Financial Planning Platform for Students." www.businesswire.com. September 21, 2021. https://tinyurl.com/2qtqtvd8.

8. Hugh Son. "JPMorgan Shutters Website It Paid $175 Million For, Accuses Founder of Inventing Millions of Accounts." CNBC. January 12, 2023. https://tinyurl.com/2pxb34ml.

9. Lee Rainie, Scott Keeter, and Andrew Perrin. "Trust and Distrust in America." Pew Research Center. July 22, 2019. https://tinyurl.com/y7zrdxfw.

10. Satoshi Nakamoto. "Bitcoin: A Peer-To-Peer Electronic Cash System." Bitcoin. https://tinyurl.com/kkxbyss.

11. Jacob Aron. "Bitcoin: How Its Core Technology Will Change the World." *New Scientist.* https://tinyurl.com/2fbnlh6p.

12. John Detrixhe. "The Simple Reason DocuSign Doesn't Use Blockchain." Quartz. December 7, 2020. https://tinyurl.com/2qh8rvjm.

13. "Legal." DocHub. December 18, 2018. https://tinyurl.com/2f223f3e.

14. Stephane Kasriel. "Skill, Re-Skill and Re-Skill Again. How to Keep Up With the Future of Work." World Economic Forum. July 31, 2017. https://tinyurl.com/2hd4op3w.

15. "Accelerating Workforce Reskilling for the Fourth Industrial Revolution." World Economic Forum. July 27, 2017. https://tinyurl.com/2qy2dokw.

16. "Project Management Institute." Credly. https://tinyurl.com/2n89qcog

17. Vishal Gaur and Abhinav Gaiha. "Building a Transparent Supply Chain." *Harvard Business Review.* May 1, 2020. https://tinyurl.com/ycbv6fat.

18. "IBM Food Trust Expands Blockchain Network to Foster a Safer, More Transparent and Efficient Global Food System." Emerson. October 8, 2018. https://tinyurl.com/2oas8h8n.

19. "A 'Natural' Rise in Sustainability Around the World." NielsenIQ. January 10, 2019. https://tinyurl.com/2jfz93f7.

20. "How Does the U.S. Healthcare System Compare to Other Countries?" Peter G. Peterson Foundation. July 19, 2022. https://tinyurl.com/2jplru4o.

21. Amanda Seitz. "Americans Give Health Care System Failing Mark: AP-NORC Poll." AP NEWS. September 12, 2022. https://tinyurl.com/2funlspx.

22. "How Can We Reduce the Cost of an Increasingly Expensive Healthcare System?" Peter G. Peterson Foundation. October 19, 2022. https://tinyurl.com/2hq8jhhe.

23. Ari Levy. "Zillow Says It's Closing Homebuying Business, Cutting 25% of Workforce; Earnings Miss Estimates." CNBC. November 2, 2021. https://tinyurl.com/2e5cfrkp.

24. Justin Malonson. "Blockchain Technology Is Revolutionizing the Real Estate Industry." *Entrepreneur.* May 19, 2022. https://tinyurl.com/2oh7v4el.

25. "Blockchain Venture Capital Funding Fell to a 12-Month Low in August." Cointelegraph. September 22, 2022. https://tinyurl.com/2nn5zv37.

26. Don Tapscott and Alex Tapscott. "Here's Why Blockchains Will Change the World." *Fortune.* May 8, 2016. https://tinyurl.com/2gnf2f2d.

27. Chris Dixon. "a16zcrypto." a16z Crypto. May 22, 2022. https://a16zcrypto.com.

28. Christopher Mims. "This 3-D Printed Icelandic Fish-Gutting Machine Contains the Secret of a Future, Less-Globalized Economy." *Wall Street Journal.* January 23, 2023. https://tinyurl.com/2osz7cja.

29. Bobby Allyn. "Deepfake Video of Zelenskyy Could Be 'Tip of the Iceberg' in Info War, Experts Warn." NPR. March 16, 2022, sec. Technology. https://tinyurl.com/y8byy6g3.

30. "Learn About Content Credentials." Adobe. October 26, 2022. https://tinyurl.com/2qxnrwcu.

31. David Pogue and David Morgan. "Creating a 'Lie Detector' for Deepfakes." CBS News. January 29, 2023. https://tinyurl.com/2edu9vg5.

32. Haya R. Hasan and Khaled Salah. "Combating Deepfake Videos Using Blockchain and Smart Contracts." IEEE Access 7 (2019): 41596-41606. https://tinyurl.com/2ntm4ld6.

CHAPTER 7

1. "A 'Game-Changer': Johns Hopkins Uses Augmented Reality to Perform Major Surgeries." CBS Baltimore. June 23, 2020. tinyurl.com/2lquf6yj.

2. "Johns Hopkins Performs Its First Augmented Reality Surgeries in Patients." Johns Hopkins Medicine. February 16, 2021. tinyurl.com/2647yk4k.

3. Sara Bencic, John O'Shea, and Darshak Sanghavi. "It's Likely Back Surgeries Are Done Too Often. Can Doctors Do Better?" Brookings. November 14, 2013. tinyurl.com/2gz5bbeb.

4. Audrey J. Weiss and Anne Elixhauser. *Trends in Operating Room Procedures in US Hospitals, 2001–2011 HCUP Statistical Brief #171*. Rockville, MD: Agency for Healthcare Research and Quality; (2014).

5. Sheryl Rosen. "Augmented Reality Spine Surgery." Comprehensive Spine Center." UConn Health, June 17, 2022. tinyurl.com/2j5mutqj.

6. Henry E. Lowood. "Virtual Reality | Computer Science." In *Encyclopædia Britannica*. https://tinyurl.com/2mgrv9u7.

7. "Augmented Reality (AR)." Gartner. https://tinyurl.com/246km5hs.

8. Paul Milgram and Fumio Kishino. 1994. "A Taxonomy of Mixed Reality Visual Displays." December 1, 1994. https://tinyurl.com/2myfxtjw.

9. Simon Greenwold. 2002. "Spatial Computing." https://tinyurl.com/2n4b5p8a.

10. Malcolm Owen. "Microsoft Layoffs Effectively Kill HoloLens & Mixed Reality Projects." *Apple Insider*. January 23, 2023. tinyurl.com/2gap4oy6.

11. Kalley Huang. "Snap Reports Slowest-Ever Quarterly Growth but Adds New Users." *New York Times*. October 20, 2022. tinyurl.com/2fyr2caj.

12. Adario Strange. "Why Meta's Ray-Ban Smart Glasses Haven't Caught on a Year after Launch." Quartz. September 12, 2022. tinyurl.com/2lzmskyw.

13. Mark Gurman. "Apple Will Talk Up Its Mixed-Reality Headset in 2023 but Not Much Else." Bloomberg.com. January 8, 2023. tinyurl.com/2kohrzeu.

14. Nicole Lewis. "Walmart Revolutionizes Its Training With Virtual Reality." SHRM. July 22, 2019. tinyurl.com/2plsomeg.

15. "Enter a New Era of Digital Change." Accenture. 2022. tinyurl.com/2erqfohr.

16. "Going Beyond With Extended Reality." Accenture. March 16, 2022. tinyurl.com/yan62k4d.

17. "Zoom Meets Virtual Reality: Announcing Zoom's Collaboration With Horizon Workrooms." Meta. September 13, 2021. https://tinyurl.com/2jta63g3.

18. "Release Notes for December 27, 2022." Zoom. December 29, 2022. https://tinyurl.com/2qv99kk3.

19. "Definition of Gamification." Merriam-Webster. https://tinyurl.com/2ptlmzgj.

20. Raed S. Alsawaier. "The Effect of Gamification on Motivation and Engagement." *International Journal of Information and Learning Technology* 35 (1): 56–79. https://doi.org/10.1108/ijilt-02-2017-0009.

21. "'Speed Camera Lottery': What If We Rewarded Drivers for Respecting Speed Limits?" RTL. June 18, 2022. https://tinyurl.com/2pmnz4k6.

22. Niloofar Abolfathi and Simone Santamaria. "Dating Disruption—How Tinder Gamified an Industry." *MIT Sloan Management Review*. February 13, 2020. https://tinyurl.com/2jl74cnw.

23. Noam Scheiber. "How Uber Uses Psychological Tricks to Push Its Drivers' Buttons." *New York Times*. April 2, 2017. https://tinyurl.com/m8tts6l.

24. Caroline O'Donovan. "Uber and Lyft Spent Hundreds of Millions to Win Their Fight Over Workers' Rights. It Worked." BuzzFeed News. November 21, 2020. https://tinyurl.com/2nhta5nb.
25. Margot Roosevelt. "Prop. 22 Is Ruled Unconstitutional, a Blow to California Gig Economy Law." *Los Angeles Times*. August 21, 2021. https://tinyurl.com/yj6egcbk.
26. Vignesh Ramachandran. "Four Causes for Zoom Fatigue and Their Solutions." Stanford News. February 23, 2021. https://tinyurl.com/y9l3gjnp.
27. David Gura. "Update: Microsoft Makes $8.5 Billion Skype Offer Official." Marketplace. May 10, 2011. https://tinyurl.com/2pyv7tn2.
28. Susanna Ray. "Video Fatigue and a Late-Night Host With No Audience Inspire a New Way to Help People Feel Together, Remotely." Microsoft. July 8, 2020. https://tinyurl.com/2pmlfl3b.
29. "Bringing Us Together." Microsoft. January 27, 2021. https://tinyurl.com/2gcl8au5.
30. "What Is Reliable Broadband and How Many Americans Have Access to It?" USA Facts. September 27, 2022. https://tinyurl.com/2gvxem2y.
31. Tom Ara et al. "Exploring the Metaverse: What Laws Will Apply?" DLA Piper. February 22, 2022. https://tinyurl.com/2zc5fmth.

CHAPTER 8
1. Eric Rynston-lobel. "Hitting a Baseball Is the Hardest Skill to Pull Off in Sports. Here's Why." *Popular Science*. August 6, 2020. https://tinyurl.com/2p6kneuw.
2. "The First Baseball Game." Official Site of the State of New Jersey. December 22, 2008. https://tinyurl.com/2na8jpt4.
3. "Major League Miscellaneous Year-By-Year Averages and Totals." Baseball Reference. https://tinyurl.com/2dtq92u9.
4. J. J. Cooper. "Home Runs, Strikeouts, and Low Averages Are Trending Throughout Baseball." www.baseballamerica.com. May 26, 2021. https://tinyurl.com/2qjcg346.
5. "Launch Angle (LA) | Glossary." Major League Baseball. January 19, 2021. https://tinyurl.com/2hathqh2.
6. "Cubs Legend Greg Maddux's Pitching Philosophy: 'It's Not a Speed Contest.'" Cubs Insiders. April 19, 2020. https://tinyurl.com/2eghc5f7.
7. Josh Sim. "MLB World Series Scores Second-Lowest TV Ratings Ever." SportsPro. November 9, 2022. https://tinyurl.com/2h2e9w2a.
8. Rick Maese. "So Many Sports, So Few Viewers: Why TV Ratings Are Way Down During the Pandemic." *Washington Post*. November 24, 2020. https://tinyurl.com/y5t429ep.
9. Maury Brown. "MLB Attendance for 2022 Down Nearly 6% From 2019, Last Year Before the Pandemic." *Forbes*. October 6, 2022. https://tinyurl.com/2ptlkvea.
10. Anthony Castrovince. "Pitch Timer, Shift Restrictions Among Announced Rule Changes for '23." MLB.com. September 9, 2022. https://tinyurl.com/2lxaownx.
11. "Honorary Degree Recipients | Penn Secretary." University of Pennsylvania. https://tinyurl.com/s5h5kj7f .
12. Alex Kemp. "Frederick Winslow Taylor: Hero of Scientific Management." QAD Blog. April 17, 2018. https://tinyurl.com/yfuyc2u8.

13. Hannah Towey. "From 'Frupidity' to 'Swag Bucks,' 16 Secret Terms Only Amazon Workers Know, and What They Mean." Business Insider. August 24, 2022. https://tinyurl.com/2pe5jq7m.

14. Kerrie Mitchell. "Amazon 2009 KC Job Posting." Express Personnel and Entertainment Weekly via the Internet Archive. March 10, 2009. https://tinyurl.com/2lhe7fue.

15. Jason Del Rey. "Leaked Amazon Memo Warns the Company Is Running Out of People to Hire." Vox. June 17, 2022. https://tinyurl.com/24xm2g4e.

16. "Digital Taylorism." The Economist. September 10, 2015. https://tinyurl.com/2mkxs7zn.

17. Jules Roscoe. "Amazon Drivers Are Still Peeing in Bottles." VICE. November 2, 2022. https://tinyurl.com/256bwrsp.

18. Ben Wigert and Annamarie Mann. "Give Performance Reviews That Actually Inspire Employees." Gallup.com. September 25, 2017. https://tinyurl.com/yfbskdvs.

19. Kathleen Doheny. "Annual Performance Review Bows Out." SHRM. January 12, 2021. https://tinyurl.com/y5f56hso.

20. Marilyn Strathern. "'Improving Ratings': Audit in the British University System." Eur Rev. 1997; 5(3): 305–321. doi:10.1017/s1062798700002660.

21. Peter Coy. "Goodhart's Law Rules the Modern World. Here Are Nine Examples." Bloomberg. March 26, 2021. https://tinyurl.com/2mq5qpa4.

22. Donald T. Campbell. "Assessing the Impact of Planned Social Change." Evaluation and Program Planning 2 (1): 67–90. https://doi.org/10.1016/0149-7189(79)90048-x.

23. Kate Conger et al. "Two Weeks of Chaos: Inside Elon Musk's Takeover of Twitter." New York Times. November 11, 2022, sec. Technology. https://tinyurl.com/2y6qanhj.

24. H. A. Landsberger. (1958). Hawthorne Revisited. Ithaca. OCLC 61637839.

25. Saul Mcleod. "The Milgram Shock Experiment." Simply Psychology. February 5, 2017. https://tinyurl.com/yawl99pt.

26. Steven D. Levitt and John A. List. "Was There Really a Hawthorne Effect at the Hawthorne Plant? An Analysis of the Original Illumination Experiments." NBER. May 28, 2009. https://www.nber.org/papers/w15016.

27. "How Technology Is Redrawing the Boundaries of the Firm." The Economist. January 8, 2023. https://tinyurl.com/2zd3kf6b.

28. Joseph B. Fuller. "Future Positive: How Companies Can Tap into Employee Optimism to Navigate Tomorrow's Workplace." Harvard Business School. May 15, 2019. https://tinyurl.com/2kg8rph5.

29. "Hybrid Work Is Just Work. Are We Doing It Wrong?" Microsoft. September 22, 2022. https://tinyurl.com/2nv7oczr.

30. Amelia Lucas. "Starbucks CEO Howard Schultz Tells Corporate Workers to Return to the Office 3 Days a Week." CNBC. January 11, 2023. https://tinyurl.com/2fs4p5tc.

31. Christopher Mims. "More Bosses Are Spying on Quiet Quitters. It Could Backfire." Wall Street Journal, September 17, 2022, sec. Tech. https://tinyurl.com/2lgqmz87.

32. "ExpressVPN Survey Shows Widespread Surveillance on Remote Workers." ExpressVPN. May 20, 2021. https://tinyurl.com/226xlpyf.

33. Michael Barbaro. "The Rise of Workplace Surveillance." New York Times. August 24, 2022, sec. Podcasts. https://tinyurl.com/2dsq64lc.

34. Sho Dewan. "Hack to Stay On 24/7." TikTok. https://tinyurl.com/2nkjpjok.

35. Helen Poitevin. "How Employee Productivity Monitoring Has Evolved—and What's Next for HR." Gartner. August 18, 2022. https://tinyurl.com/2nh5dsze.

36. Jo Constantz. "Middle Managers Are Not Alright. Caught in the Crossfire Over Remote Work, They're Most at Risk of Burnout." *Fortune.* October 22, 2022. https://tinyurl.com/2qev9muz.

CHAPTER 9

1.   "What Was the First PC?" Computer History Museum. https://tinyurl.com/2mftd7am.

2.   Lee Felsenstein. "Oral History of John Blankenbaker." https://tinyurl.com/2fvzbnlv.

3.   "How to Start Investing for as Little as 1 Dollar." Robinhood. May 20, 2022. https://tinyurl.com/2ox69hux.

4.   Paul Sullivan. "How a Real Estate Concept from the Middle Ages Can Still Backfire." *New York Times.* June 7, 2019, sec. Your Money. https://tinyurl.com/yyg7xzm9.

5.   Kasey Tross. "Pros and Cons of Fractional Ownership." Pacaso. March 4, 2021. https://tinyurl.com/2j3ch2r6.

6.   "Pacaso to Accept Cryptocurrency Payments for Purchases of Second Homes." Pacaso. October 20, 2021. https://tinyurl.com/2otccskp.

7.   Lorna Sheridan. "Protests and Legal Action Follow Pacaso's North Bay Listings." *North Bay Business Journal.* May 22, 2021. https://tinyurl.com/2mses8lt.

8.   Konrad Putzier. "America's Office Glut Started Decades before Pandemic." *Wall Street Journal.* August 23, 2022. https://tinyurl.com/2jhh8j7v.

9.   "Who We Are." Up for Growth. September 28, 2022. https://tinyurl.com/2mxbhoft.

10. Chris Arnold et al. "There's a Massive Housing Shortage Across the U.S. Here's How Bad It Is Where You Live." NPR. July 14, 2022. https://tinyurl.com/253oqyv4.

11. Ben Wigert and Sangeeta Agrawal. "Returning to the Office: The Current, Preferred and Future State of Remote Work." Gallup. August 31, 2022. https://tinyurl.com/2m4ed5gc.

12. Angie Basiouny. "What's Going to Happen to All Those Empty Office Buildings?" Knowledge at Wharton. February 28, 2022. https://tinyurl.com/2gvd5d79.

13. Natalie Wong. "NYC's Silverstein to Raise $1.5 Billion for Office-To-Housing Push." Bloomberg. December 5, 2022. https://tinyurl.com/2fnawdts.

14. Jason Herring. "Three Downtown Calgary Office Buildings Converting to Residential." Vancouversun. June 19, 2022. https://tinyurl.com/2dt6b43k.

15. Dror Poleg. "Housing Is the New Office." Rethinking with Dror Poleg. December 6, 2022. https://tinyurl.com/2fgwe6dm.

16. Patrick Sisson. "Getting Creative with Vacant Office Space: Storage, Gym, Film Set." *New York Times.* December 27, 2022. https://tinyurl.com/2zgn9m3r.

17. Patrick Sisson. "Getting Creative with Vacant Office Space: Storage, Gym, Film Set." *New York Times.* December 27, 2022. https://tinyurl.com/2zgn9m3r.

18. Kevin Truong. "This SF Startup Wants to Be the Airbnb of Commercial Real Estate." The San Francisco Standard. December 21, 2022. https://tinyurl.com/2hlkd6re.

19. Iris Dorbian. "Office Leasing Startup Codi Inks $16m Series A." *Venture Capital Journal.* September 15, 2022. https://tinyurl.com/2zuqcfls.

20. "Five Biggest Areas of Corporate Spending Waste." Accenture. https://tinyurl.com/2ffj8syw.

21. Nate Berg. "Fortune 500 Companies Are Wasting Millions on Unused Office Space." Fast Company. https://tinyurl.com/2e5ne72l.

22. "2022 Contingent Faculty Survey." American Federation of Teachers. August 19, 2022. https://tinyurl.com/26wj8lkc.

23. Colleen Flaherty. "New Report Says Many Adjuncts Make Less than $3,500 per Course and $25,000 per Year." Inside Higher Ed. April 20, 2020. https://tinyurl.com/27nrloe2.

24. Scott Galloway. "Higher Education in the US Has Become Un-American." Business Insider. November 19, 2021. https://tinyurl.com/2aa4s77k.

25. "Why Colleges and Universities Must Control Runaway Spending." American Council of Trustees and Alumni Institute for Effective Governance. August 15, 2021. https://tinyurl.com/2d36vss9.

26. Adam Satariano and Mike Isaac. "The Silent Partner Cleaning Up Facebook for $500 Million a Year." *New York Times*. August 31, 2021, sec. Technology. https://tinyurl.com/yhauqean.

27. "Employer Costs for Employee Compensation News Release." Bureau of Labor Statistics. December 15, 2022. https://tinyurl.com/hybs97u.

28. Mark Maurer. "More Finance Chiefs Resigned in 2020 Than in Previous Years." *Wall Street Journal*. January 18, 2021, sec. C Suite. https://tinyurl.com/2z2ncnua.

29. Amy Hood. "LinkedIn Profile." LinkedIn. https://tinyurl.com/2dnakdv8.

CHAPTER 10

1. "Estimated Advertising and Circulation Revenue of the Newspaper Industry." Pew Research Center. June 29, 2021. https://tinyurl.com/2gpsj8ac.

2. David Bauder and David Lieb. "More Than 1,400 Cities and Towns in U.S. Have Lost Newspapers in Past 15 Years." *South Bend Tribune*. March 11, 2019. https://tinyurl.com/2eawg275.

3. Kristen Hare. "More Than 100 Local Newsrooms Closed During the Coronavirus Pandemic." Poynter. December 2, 2021. https://tinyurl.com/2zp42qdu.

4. "The CUNY Graduate School of Journalism Receives $20 Million Gift from Craig Newmark, Founder of Craigslist and Craig Newmark Philanthropies." CUNY Newswire. June 18, 2018. https://tinyurl.com/2er6oqh4.

5. Grace Ashford and Michael Gold. "Who Is Rep.-Elect George Santos? His Résumé May Be Largely Fiction." *New York Times*. December 19, 2022, sec. New York. https://tinyurl.com/2jhf2qat.

6. Neil Vigdor. "George Santos Is in a Class of His Own. But Other Politicians Have Embellished Their Resumes, Too." *New York Times*. December 28, 2022, sec. U.S. https://tinyurl.com/2js55cyg.

7. Mychael Schnell. "Ethics Watchdog Files FEC Complaint against George Santos." *The Hill*. January 9, 2023. https://tinyurl.com/2qj96onb.

8. Noam Laden. "Republican Asks George Santos to Resign." WABC. January 1, 2023. https://tinyurl.com/2kshcl2z.

9. Bruce Daisley. "The Work-From-Anywhere War Is Beginning." Wired UK. December 29, 2022. https://tinyurl.com/2dvmhxgj.

10. Rani Molla. "Most Americans Like Remote Work—but Democrats Like It More." Vox. July 17, 2021. https://tinyurl.com/27fk34hk.

11. "Newsweek to Cease Print Edition After 80 Years." CBS 8. October 18, 2012. https://tinyurl.com/2hy8s2m8.

12. Sarah Ellison. "The Washington Post Will End Its Sunday Magazine, Eliminate Positions." *Washington Post*. November 30, 2022. https://tinyurl.com/2gqlckmy.

13. Michael Kozlowski. "Barnes and Noble Will Stop Selling New Magazines." Good E-Reader. April 26, 2020. https://tinyurl.com/2ohnvfrd.

14. "Circuit City to Fire More Than 3,400 Workers." NBC News. March 28, 2007. https://tinyurl.com/2gvjt6qn.

15. Rachel Beck. "Lessons in How Circuit City's Job Cuts Backfired." SFGATE. January 13, 2008. https://tinyurl.com/2zo7nbap.

16. Kevin Kelleher. "How the Geek Squad Could Be Best Buy's Secret Weapon." *Time*. July 19, 2016. https://tinyurl.com/2ogu9uqf.

17. Leslie P. Norton. "The 100 Most Sustainable U.S. Companies." *Barron's*. February 8, 2019. https://tinyurl.com/y623hap2.

18. Jay Greene. "Amazon May Have Used Proprietary Data to Compete with Its Merchants, Bezos Tells Congress." *Washington Post*. July 29, 2020. https://tinyurl.com/2ba4xsbm.

19. Patrick Sisson. "The Company That Powers Allbirds and Kylie Jenner Is Coming for Amazon." Vox. January 23, 2020. https://tinyurl.com/v93my57.

20. Michael Sainato. "Trader Joe's Broke Labor Laws in Effort to Stop Stores Unionizing, Workers Say." *The Guardian*. September 4, 2022. https://tinyurl.com/2gww2vy4.

21. Milton Friedman. "The Social Responsibility of Business Is to Increase Its Profits." *New York Times*. September 13, 1970. https://tinyurl.com/yyzk445k.

22. Lynn Stout. "Corporations Don't Have to Maximize Profits." *New York Times*. April 16, 2015. https://tinyurl.com/y73jutbs.

23. "One Year Later: Purpose of a Corporation." Business Roundtable. August 19, 2019. https://purpose.businessroundtable.org/.

24. Suntae Kim et al. "Why Companies Are Becoming B Corporations." *Harvard Business Review*. June 17, 2016. https://tinyurl.com/zfjhgth.

25. "How Many Certified B Corps Are There Around the World?" B Lab. January 23, 2022. https://tinyurl.com/2myaxqed.

26. Sean Peek. "What Is a B Corp? Advantages and Requirements." US Chamber of Commerce. May 5, 2020. https://tinyurl.com/22bk28yq.

27. Greg Lewis. "The Jobs With the Highest Turnover Rates, According to LinkedIn Data." LinkedIn. June 30, 2022. https://tinyurl.com/2q8szprz.

28. Kathryn Dill. "Your Next Boss: More Harmony, Less Authority." *Wall Street Journal*. January 12, 2021, sec. Life. https://tinyurl.com/y344fnc7.

29. Bobby Allyn. "A Robot Was Scheduled to Argue in Court, Then Came the Jail Threats." NPR. January 25, 2023. https://tinyurl.com/2l64dvay.